The Crossroads up Should & must – Find & Follow your Passion –
Elle Turner

Heart to Heart

The Path to Wellness

Sarah Prout and Sean Patrick Simpson

Älska Publishing

Älska means to LOVE
(Say it like this: elsh-ka)

The Heart to Heart Series: Volume #1
First published 2015 by Älska Publishing

Office based in Noosa Heads, Australia

© Sarah Prout and Sean Patrick Simpson

The moral rights of the authors have been asserted

National Library of Australia Cataloguing-in-Publication entry:

Authors:	Prout, Sarah 1979 -- / Simpson, Sean Patrick 1984 --
Title:	Heart to Heart: The Path to Wellness
ISBN:	9780994186508 (pbk) 9780994186515 (ebook : kindle) 9780994186522 (ebook : epub)
Subjects:	Well-being, health, inspiration, self-care, self-actualization
Dewey Number:	158.1

Cover design, formatting, editing and ebook conversion by Verbii.com – an Älska Publishing company.

Printed in Hong Kong

Also available in electronic format.

www.AlskaPublishing.com

Wholesale Discounts
For competitive rates on bulk purchases, please go to www.AlskaPublishing.com

Disclaimer
The material in this publication is of the nature of general comment only and does not represent professional advice. To the maximum extent permitted by the law, the authors and publisher disclaim all responsibility and liability to any person, arising directly or indirectly from an person taking or not taking action based upon the information in this publication.

Dedication

To you, the reader, may this book inspire you to discover your own journey on the path to wellness.

To my Dearest Kathy —

How can I express my gratitude for all your love, caring concern, prayers and presence during the most traumatic time of my life. Your beautiful love + light helped me find my way out of the darkness and I am eternally grateful —

I treasure + love you beyond measure,

Mary

Acknowledgments

We honor you for everything you are:

Our Älska authors, who made this book possible – thank you for persevering through life's challenges and using its lessons as an opportunity to grow in consciousness and to inspire those around you. This world is a better place because of you.

Our parents - who have showered us with their gifts of love and determination to give us the best life they could.

Our children – who chose us and give us the most powerful reminders to love unconditionally.

Our students and readers – who have continued to inspire us with passion and purpose.

Our mentors and friends – we wouldn't be who we are today without your love, guidance, and acceptance of everything we are.

With Love & Gratitude,
Sarah Prout and Sean Patrick Simpson

Contents

Conclusions

Introduction

I t is with soul-felt gratitude that we would like to welcome you to the Heart to Heart series.

Heart to Heart: The Path to Wellness is an extraordinary collection of true-life experiences written from the hearts and minds of more than 40 inspiring authors.

The stories shared in this book are miraculous and cover the full range of how strong the human spirit can be when faced with extreme adversity.

The authors within were not gifted with any more special abilities or opportunities than you have. They have simply been gifted with the experience of life, as well as the opportunity to look within for strength, courage, and perseverance—gifts that are open to all of us should we choose to accept them.

One thing we know with absolute certainty is that your heart grows in direct proportion to your own courage. And you are given the opportunity for this expansion on a daily basis with one of life's most powerful teachers: *uncertainty.*

More often than not, the experiences of massive uncertainty can put your heart and soul into a holding space where you're not entirely sure what the outcome of your situation will be. The only choice for getting through it is to surrender *into* the experience, to embrace both the "good" and the "bad" with all your heart, and to focus your attention on wellness in each and every moment.

Through the varying journeys of 40+ authors, *The Path to Wellness* will show you exactly how to do that, and will be a powerful reminder that the human spirit *is* beyond incredible—and that sometimes our greatest challenges are also our greatest gifts.

We hope you enjoy this collection of inspiring stories, and wish you the best on your own journey down the path to wellness.

With Love and Gratitude,

Sarah Prout and Sean Patrick Simpson
Co-Founders Älska Publishing
Co-Creators of the Heart to Heart series

Cages of the Mind

—————⚹—————

Gretchen M. Fox

Cages come in many different forms. No matter the type, whenever I feel confined or trapped, it is a cage. The worst cages are the ones you create with your mind. These cages are much harder to break free from, for the mind is stronger than any metal. I know, for this is where I lived for many years.

He is dying. . . . The breaths are slower. His eyes are dull and empty. His soul has already left his body. One breath. Pause. Another breath. Pause. The next breath does not come. He is gone and I am now alone. The tears rain down my cheeks. Disbelief, numbness, shock. I call his Mom, the kids, my sister, and wait.

Diagnosed with cancer six weeks earlier, my husband of thirty-one years had died. The first few days were filled with phone calls, arrangements, family, friends, and the funeral. After a week, everyone had gone and returned to their everyday lives. I am alone in an empty house with silent walls and a heavy heart. My home became a physical cage as I hid from the world—from myself.

What now? How do I live alone? It has been over thirty years since I shared space with only myself. Who am I now? How do I cope? How do I learn to live? Where do I begin? I felt as though I had died with my husband—and too scared to move in any direction. I was so lost.

I view my life as normal by most standards. I grew up as the middle child of seven and spent a lot of time with extended family. It was fun! While every family is dysfunctional in some way, I feel like mine is okay. We are always there for each other. I did the usual stuff: grew up, went to college, got a job, got married, and had a couple of kids. It was a fairly normal life on the outside. On the inside, I lived in a cage, trapped by my own fears and frustrations. I had isolated myself from the world for so long that I was not really sure how to live in it again. Since grad school, I have been quiet, observing the world around me and the people in it. I let myself be controlled, not guided. I hid myself away and let the flow of life wash over me without taking part. I only have myself to blame because I allowed it to happen. I didn't know a way out of myself—out of the cages of my mind.

I had no idea of who I was or where I was going. I was suddenly free to discover me, and it was scary as hell! I had always defined myself by the people around me, by my job, by what I did or didn't do, and not by who I really am. I had a whole lifetime in front of me. Yet I had no job, no husband, no goals, no ideas, and I was grieving too many losses.

Not a pretty picture.

Grief is one of the hardest cages to escape from. It not only confines you physically, but also mentally, emotionally, and spiritually. This cage is one of isolation, pain, fear, anger, and frustration. I was constantly questioning myself, my life, my late husband. Could we have done more? Why was it so hard? Who is to blame? Is there anyone to blame? Does it even matter?

I wanted to finally put the questions to rest and started searching for the answers. I wanted direction and hope and to be fulfilled as the person I knew was in there, somewhere—*the me*—who I had put on hold while I lived a life as a wife, a mother, a daughter, a friend. I had put myself in all types of unique cages over the years.

In order to break free, I went through some nasty muck! While I had accepted my husband's death, I was really angry, hurt, and resentful. Little stuff kept cropping up in my mind about how our lives had played out. Too often I had felt that his attention and affection was elsewhere. Too many times I felt unloved, unwanted, abandoned, and alone in our marriage. It was easy to place all the blame on him. He wasn't here to defend himself. It really didn't make me feel any better though. I realized I had to move *through* the anger, the pain, the fear, the frustration, and the hurt that I felt if I wanted to get to the other side. I did see the light, but it seemed so far away and hard to reach. Throughout my life I had compromised so much of myself away, I didn't even know who I was or what I wanted. I hated this cage most of all. It was a cage of a lost soul with no identity.

I didn't know what to do with my life. I only knew I wanted to make a difference in people's lives, somehow, in some way. I was born to teach and heal. I have always known this, but had denied it most of my life.

I took classes, went to seminars, traveled, meditated, danced. The closer I came to the answer, it slipped away, hiding around the next bend, luring me—just out of reach like a carrot on a stick. I grew impatient, frustrated, and angry. What I didn't realize was how much of this had to do with the grief I had pushed down and away. It was a cage that I couldn't see, but I felt it. I felt like I had no one to turn to, no one to talk to, no way out. I not only felt trapped, but also terribly alone. There were days I felt so clear on what my next steps were, and I moved in that direction. Then, the next day, just like that, I was

befuddled all over again. While I ventured outside my cage, hoping to break free, I always found myself back inside. It felt safe.

I continued to search, explore, and process, but it wasn't until I learned to *forgive* that everything changed. I learned not only to forgive the perceived things my late husband did or didn't do, but I learned to forgive myself. I stopped placing blame and took responsibility for my own thoughts, my own feelings, and my own life. I was feeling happier, freer, and more aware. I started to shake off the confinements of my cage. As I embraced the knowledge that I am Divinely guided, I learned to love and trust myself.

I began to *wake up* and extend myself beyond even my own expectations. I traveled to new places, learned new things, and pushed myself way outside my comfort zone. I followed my passion for healing and became a Spiritual Response Therapy (SRT) consultant. I followed my passion for teaching and became a life coach.

I would be lying if I said I was completely healed and living fully. I am a work in progress. I am always reaching beyond my cage—toward the light. As I spread my light to embrace others, I have noticed that the bars on my cage are slowly disappearing with each step I take out into the world. I am leaving the cages of my mind behind and following my heart.

It has been several years since the passing of my husband and other loved ones close to me. It has not always been easy, but I no longer let the grief define me or rule my life. I know it is hard to move beyond the cages you may have created, and you may often feel alone. We are here to help each other shine, heal, and learn to stand on our stories and not in them. Forgive. Leave blame behind. Take responsibility for your own life and happiness. All the answers are within you. You only need to escape the cages of the mind and to listen to your heart!

About the Author

Gretchen M. Fox is a certified life coach and SRT consultant with spiritual healing, grief, and loss expertise. She has learned to believe in herself and released fear to create a happy, loving, and fulfilling life. Gretchen can help you do the same. She is also the author of *Raising a Child's Awareness*, guiding children to be happier and more empowered.

http://www.yourinspiredheart.net

Return to Your Garden of Eden

Hilde Van Schuerbeek

As a little child, I felt cherished and protected from any possible harm as if I never left the womb. My life was charming, wonderful, and harmonious. We kept rabbits, cats, dogs, sheep, and chickens. They all had a name and their own play area outside, just like me. I had a huge garden with a natural pond surrounded by a beautiful forest full of wildlife. I spent hours talking to the birds in the trees, the cats on my lap, my hamsters, and the rabbits and sheep on the green grass. My greatest joy was to go for a walk in the woods with my family and dog. It was my family who pointed out the beauty of nature to me. I learned to love and respect life, to enjoy the smell of the trees, the colors of the leaves, the rain, the sun, the wind, and the clouds. I had a deep loving connection with all of life on the planet. We were one. I could not have wished for anything more beautiful.

I must have been about five years old at the time; I came home from school and did not see my white rabbit in its hutch. It was gone. I found it hanging upside down in a shelter at the back of the garden, stripped of its skin. This gruesome picture is still engraved in my brain. I gasped for air and ran inside to get some help. I learned my loving grandfather killed rabbits for food, and my entire family thought it was okay. I was shocked, helpless, and confused. Soon, I discovered chickens and sheep had disappeared. And, although not for food, kittens went missing. I lay down and cried beside the

5

lifeless bodies of mice and insects. Where was my Garden of Eden? The cord was cut off.

I was born into the real world.

My family explained to me that animals were kept for food and that we did not have enough space to keep them all. It was silly to cry for a rabbit. Although nobody wanted to hurt me, I felt emotionally unsafe and different. There was nobody I could fully trust. I felt lonely and scared. The pain became my secret. Though I never ate rabbit again in my entire life, and kept my fascination and love for the natural world, I blocked the whole idea that animals became the food on my plate. I refused reality and went back to my comfortable life. The need to belong, to be accepted and loved dulled my passion and connection.

The first thing I closed off were my ears. Not only were people avoiding the subject when talking to me, I also did not want to hear the truth. I literally developed regular blockages of ear wax followed by ear infections. When I was about fourteen years old, I started developing allergies to all kinds of animal and natural substances, interestingly not to rabbits: the only "food" that was not on my plate. I was regularly plagued with colds, chest tightness, pulmonary infections, wheezing, and shortness of breath. Four years later, I was diagnosed with severe asthma and was hospitalized for a lack of oxygen at least twice a year. My lung specialist at that time told me that there was no cure for asthma and that I would probably never be able to bear any children.

One night, at the age of twenty-two, I was standing in front of the window, trying to get more air. I couldn't breathe, and I started panicking. It crossed my mind for one moment to jump, since I viewed my condition as unendurable. Fortunately, I still had a longing for life and made a better decision. I started reading books about health. I read one after the other, but did not really change much to my diet or lifestyle until a single sentence in one of those books caught my attention. It said something like, "If you see a squirrel right in front of you, do you go after it, kill it with your bare hands, and put your teeth in its raw flesh?" *Who would do such a thing!*

I then suddenly realized I was. How could I do such a thing! Even though I could not kill an animal with my own bare hands or teeth, I let others execute it for me. How could I possibly think that it was okay? Why would I eat a cow or a pig and not a squirrel or a rabbit? What I had been doing my entire life was going against my personal core values of fairness, compassion, love, and empathy. I realized that I was the one who cut the cords and disconnected myself from what I was so passionate about: animals and nature! These two were, and still are, my source of oxygen and life energy.

I became a vegetarian on that very same day. The symptoms cleared up very quickly, and six months later my asthma completely disappeared. I stopped taking all types of medication, from steroids to inhalers, and did not have a single attack for more than twenty-six years. Research shows that a meat-based diet poses a risk for asthma. Animal products cause an inflammatory reaction within hours of consumption, and emotional stress can intensify clinical symptoms in patients with asthma.

There may or may not be a biological pathway to explain my miraculous cure. What I do know is that I had started to listen to my own body and to trust my inner guidance. Awareness of the separation of my body, mind, and spirit was one of the first steps in this whole healing process. I reconnected with my essential self, my source of oxygen, and life itself. I even gave birth to two beautiful, healthy children.

But this is not the end of the story.

When we moved to a highly polluted city for my husband's job, I was warned about the negative health effects, especially on people with sensitive airways. Sure enough, after four months living there, my asthma reappeared! I was puzzled. Despite the fact that I had become vegan for 95 percent of the time, was taking great care of getting all the nutrients my body needed, and despite the powerful air purifier we bought for our home and the many complementary therapies, the asthma was back. Only this time, I was convinced not to obscure reality and not to turn a blind eye to my soul. What message was my body trying to convey? What did I ignore or what was I disconnected from? Obviously, pollution was one reason, being disconnected from nature another—but what more did I need to learn?

There was more work to do than to assume the obvious. Another obstruction had to be cleared, a deeper lying message revealed. While I discovered my core values, I still did not bring them passionately alive and let them roar. Time had come to share the gifts of my garden. It was my dream to help people experience the incredible healing power of connecting with their source of energy and to encourage compassion, love, and empathy for all life on Earth. I had to start spinning with the thread of life to return to my Garden of Eden. Incorporating mutual beneficial interactions with animals and nature in my work was one way to do this. I also needed to make new plans for my personal life and finally live my dream. It was my deepest desire to connect and surround myself with the natural world. I had to find my tribe who share that longing. Taking actions in that direction gradually improved my asthma once again, although I hadn't yet left the polluted city.

Nutrition plays a very important role in your health and wellbeing and so do your thoughts, beliefs, social and physical environment, and emotional wellbeing. If you want to take your health to new horizons, you will have to scratch a little deeper though. Whenever you feel unfulfilled, sick, unhappy, or can't reach your full potential, I urge you to stop and listen. Crack the code of your aches and pains and listen to the messages they deliver rather than to dwell in distress. Feel what is alive in you, focus on what inspires you, and fan the flames of your soul for it is the source of energy that influences and nourishes your entire being.

When you feel stuck, let somebody guide you to rise above limitations, obstacles, old patterns, and wounds, and to unlock new doors. Tune into nature, recognize your interconnectedness, allow any animal, place, or element that exerts a pull on you to reveal its wisdom and feed you on an energetic level. With these insights and fresh perspectives, you can make new decisions and positive changes that nourish your body, mind, and spirit. No matter where you are in your life, you have a choice to pick up the thread that pulls you together and leads you back to the whole.

I strongly believe that there is no one golden path to wellness. Each journey is unique. Stay present and alert, and start traveling from where you are. *Bon voyage!*

About the Author

Hilde Van Schuerbeek offers health coaching to individuals and groups to reclaim their passion, joy, and health. Her approach to healing is holistic and based on recognizing our uniqueness and interconnectedness. She advocates wholesome food and mutual beneficial interactions with animals and nature to boost your immune system and energy levels. She empowers you to identify goals that are in alignment with your true self and to create feasible, enjoyable, and personalized action plans.

http://www.take-your-health-to-new-horizons.com

Calm in the Midst
of the Storm

---❦---

Dr. Mary Sidhwani

I t is a little chilly in the hospital examining room. I am on a steel cold table and, though a numbing agent is used, I can feel the pain and discomfort. Poking and prodding continue during this breast biopsy brought about by an abnormal mammogram. I feel a machine come up beneath me and repeatedly throughout the hour-long procedure, clamping and twisting the right breast. They are attempting to locate the abnormal site seen on the mammogram. Though everyone is extremely kind, my mind is reeling, and the pain and fear are increasing.

I thought I was somewhat prepared for this as I had previously been a registered nurse for many years. During those fifteen years, I had witnessed much pain and trauma, which had drawn me to learn more about the mind and how to alleviate emotional and mental suffering. Fourteen years ago, I returned to school to receive a Master's in clinical hypnotherapy and later a Doctorate in counseling psychology. As I lay on the table, I knew I had to put into practice the knowledge and tools I had been blessed to share with my patients in private practice. Utilizing the wisdom of the tremendous power of the inner mind, practical and effective ways used to help my patients through the storms in their lives.

There are many storms in life, such as financial and relationship issues, health crisis, abuse, loss, and grief among others. Though your story may not be my story, I would be honored to share the healing techniques I used with the power of the mind to calm and transform the storm in my life.

As I lay on that table during the biopsy procedure, I knew I had to find a point of focus in order to distract myself and help calm my mind. Thus, I focused intently upon a photo on the wall; the vivid colors of orange and red drew me in as I breathed deeply and slowly. This is a technique that can be used at anytime whenever we are faced with a challenge and need to calm the mind. At home, in a waiting room, at work, we can shift our focus away from the frightening and upsetting thoughts. All you need to do is find a focal point, such as a clock, a picture, a cloud, or a sign, and bring all of your attention to that object. Then begin breathing deeply and slowly at least five times as you notice this object, the color, the shape, its texture or sound. This brings us to a place of being grounded and centered and helps us cope more effectively with whatever is occurring around or within us. Doing this not only calmed me, but also distorted time so that it went by more quickly. The nurses asked me what I was doing in order to remain so calm and still. I promised I would share it with them after the procedure and teach them the technique.

A week goes by and, in between patients, I am constantly checking for a message from my surgeon. I am utilizing the above technique in order to cope throughout the day and effectively be there for my patients and family. The phone rings, and I hear the surgeon saying that I do have breast cancer. My knees buckle, I feel as if the floor opened up beneath me, and I am falling into darkness. I am struggling to hear what he is saying as my mind reels, and I find myself groping in the dark. Though he is very compassionate, he speaks for a very long time about statistics, percentages, and worst case scenarios.

Surgery needs to be scheduled immediately, followed by radiation therapy. I feel as if I cannot breathe. We schedule a surgery date—and I sit there stunned and traumatized after the call is over. My head is swimming with data, percentages, and statistics, and I realize that in Western society we look at this information to save us during our storms in life. Whatever the storm may be, we gather information from outside ourselves, arming ourselves with this data. Though it is very important to gather information to understand what is happening and to make an informed decision, it is just as vitally important to tap into the power of the inner mind.

We forget, or most likely do not realize, that the conscious mind is only 10 percent of our power; 90 percent of our power comes from the unconscious/subconscious mind, which I refer to as the inner mind.

In my practice, I teach patients about the power of the inner mind and how it is comparable to a CD or tape recorder. It is the repository of all we have experienced, received, and recorded since our souls first came into existence. Though we may not consciously recall this information, it exists within the inner mind. As we tap into this tremendous power, we bring forth wisdom, strength, understanding, and empowerment. Through my years of learning and helping others through the trials in their lives, I knew I had to tap into the inner mind in order to bring me through this trauma. Please know that the following techniques I utilized to transform the terror into strength and calmness can be used to move through any storm in your life.

Immediately after receiving the news, I could not sleep. Though my wonderful husband, two children, family, and friends were extremely supportive and loving, my mind would race with all the information shared by the surgeon. I would lay awake at night and go over the worst case scenarios, my heart pounding in fear.

Once again, my mind turns to my practice and what I have learned throughout the years. Having recorded many CDs for patients, I downloaded those guided healing meditations onto my MP3 device. Whenever I would awaken during the night, which were many times, I would immediately replay a meditation. I knew that, as I repeated this, it would reprogram my inner mind with positive, life-affirming, and nurturing thoughts. As the mind learns through repetition, slowly my mind began to calm—my sleep became more restful.

In addition to my private practice, I also teach self-hypnosis to guide others in overcoming obstacles and reaching important goals in life. To cope with my fear and anxiety, I took myself into hypnosis for approximately fifteen minutes each day. I would like to briefly describe this powerful technique that will effectively transform any challenge in your life.

First, write down three affirmations on an index c[…]
words "I am" before each statement to align with the pow[…]
mind and the spiritual connection within each of us. For [...]
I wrote, "I am calm, strong, and balanced", "I am the po[...]
healing," and "I am happy and peaceful." Next, read over each
affirmation three times. Then find a quiet place to relax and begin
inhaling deeply and exhaling slowly five times. Close your eyes and
allow all those tiny muscles and tissues in and around your eyes to
become soft and heavy. Imagine a safe and peaceful place and spend
a few minutes here. Now imagine the storm in your life resolved.
What does that look like? What does that feel like? Bring in as many
of the five senses as you can and stay here for approximately ten
minutes. Then say to yourself that you will be back in a wide-awake,
fully alert state when you open your eyes. You can carry this index
card with you and read it throughout the day for reinforcement and
reassurance.

As you do this each day, you are programming your mind with
what you want to happen, what you desire for your life.

As spiritual writings tell us, you can be transformed by the
renewing of your mind. The inner mind is also the bridge between
the ego and higher self, thus strengthening our connection to God/
Spirit. Practicing self hypnosis each day allows the positive thoughts
to merge with the feelings of the heart in order to become balanced
and healed in mind, body, and spirit.

Each day, I envisioned the surgery going well and recovering
easily and smoothly. On October 30, 2013, I underwent the
lumpectomy. It did indeed go well; the pathology report showed no
need for further surgery, and I recovered quickly.

My next challenge was to undergo daily radiation for one month.
I was extremely worried about what it could do to my body and how
I would cope with going every day while maintaining a full-time
practice and caring for my family. So as I practiced self hypnosis
daily, I saw myself and felt myself easily balancing everything.
In addition, I envisioned the radiation beams as white light that
would prevent the cancer from recurring but would not harm me
in any way. I also utilized my focus and breathing technique during
treatment as I had to remain perfectly still for those twenty-minute
sessions.

As treatment was ending, I could see how the storms and challenges in our lives equal transformation. As we tap into the power of the mind, we find strengths, resources, and wisdom, all which bring us through these challenges and remain with us.

My experience strengthened my connection to God/Spirit deeply, my heart understands from a different place, my work continues to come from this deeper level of compassion. By learning the way through the darkness of my storm, my intent, deepest desire, and hope is that my story may carry you through your own storm safely. Calming, reassuring you, and bringing you to the healing you so deserve.

About the Author

Dr. Mary Sidhwani is a psychotherapist specializing in hypnotherapy and has been in private practice since 2000. Dr. Sidhwani is also an RN with certifications in clinical hypnosis and cancer support. Her commitment and honor is to help others through the trials of chronic illness and any emotional challenges with compassionate understanding. Dr. Sidhwani is also a professional speaker who has presented at NASA and other institutions and authored the CD series *Recognize the Truth Within.*

http://www.womenstherapeutic.com

Thank you, Good Bye
I am Calm & Strong

A Natural High

Shannon Nicole

It had been ten-plus years since I last experienced the sweet numbing sensation of alcohol caressing my lips. I sipped cautiously, knowing all too well what could happen as a result. I needed it to quench my thirst, which was more of a spiritual hankering than actual hydration. I even said a prayer before I put the glass to my mouth, asking God to be with me while I experimented with what I already knew separated me from Him. I had to. I needed to know. Somewhere in the past year, I bought into the delusion that because of all the healing work I'd done, I might be able to drink like a normal person. With all my imagination, I fantasized a "silver screen style" picture of being a social drinker. After all, they made it look so glamorous, and, once again, I wanted to belong to that group—to be like them. But, deep down, it was much more than that.

And I knew it.

It only took one glass for me to figure out I wasn't that person anymore. After ten years of sobriety, I had some sense of what sanity was—and this was not it. What had once been an obsessive desire, an insatiable craving now felt awkward, uncomfortable, and phony. I silently asked myself why I was doing it. I was comfortable in my own skin. I didn't need it to have fun in social situations anymore. What was I looking for? In spite of the painstaking journey I had taken for freedom, I kept drinking, noticing every euphoric rush, giddy laugh, and uninhibited word I spoke. I felt ridiculous. One was enough, but the ride wasn't over.

The following day, the spiritual plummet cast me onto the couch, in guilty tears, and the emotional darkness hovered over me like a thick cloud. I swore I'd never do it again. A week later I did. It was the beginning of a cycle I knew all too well. The terrain had been well-traveled, hauntingly familiar, and long since been relinquished for higher ground. In the midst of my slip, I had forgotten how rocky and desolate the past excursion had been.

When I took a closer look and reviewed the bigger picture, I saw how the fear of facing the future led me to run toward the past. I had just finished writing and publishing a memoir, a story of personal transformation and an eighteen-year-old dream. At the height of my celebration, I took a dive into sheer terror, not knowing what to do next or how to navigate into the industry. I had just ended a relationship with an unavailable man, a long-standing pattern I couldn't stop repeating and was frustrated beyond measure. I felt stagnant and unhappy at my job, and even Alcoholics Anonymous, the place that gave me a spiritual foundation, wasn't filling me up anymore. Who was I if I wasn't participating in a heart wrenching relationship? Where was the joy in my life when I actively sought God and to be of service in the world? Why was I constantly filled with the fear of not being good enough? How do I stand confidently as an author and have faith in myself? Why did I have such a fruitless experience manifesting all that I desire?

The questions only enforced my unworthiness. I felt backed into a corner. I knew something had to change, quickly. I curled up, turned to the Heavens and whimpered, "Help me!"

Not long after, on an intuitive impulse, I signed up for a workshop called the *Wonder Woman Weekend* facilitated by Iyanla Vanzant and a team of fourteen spiritual and holistic practitioners. I knew her then as an author and motivational speaker. I had read some of her books, and, over time, her many appearances on the *Oprah Winfrey Show* caught my attention. More recently, I had signed up for her email blasts after seeing her new television series called *Iyanla: Fix My Life*. I thought it would be fun and would get me out of my rut. I had no idea the profound impact it would have on my life, the shifts it would bring, the connections it would hold, the healing we would share, and the truths I would gain.

There are no words sufficient enough for an experience so spiritually powerful. What I can tell you is somewhere in the middle of this amazing process, I sat with my eyes closed, having my vibration lifted through music and being prayed over by healing masters. Somewhere in the darkness of the *not good enough's*, I got a glimpse of what was underneath. I saw the flame of my divine light—the essence of who I am.

In that moment, all the misconceptions of who I believed I was melted away. In divine order, I subsequently received an unmistakable "calling" to attend the Inner Visions Institute for Spiritual Development also founded by Iyanla Vanzant. I was about to embark on a new journey. It was time to create a new chapter in my life. We would begin by healing on all four levels of my being: spiritual, mental, emotional, and physical.

Healing our internal being is the way to health and harmony of body, mind, and spirit. It's not just about going to church, eating healthy, or being intellectual. It's about going within and clearing out all the things that block us from having our fullest expression in the world: the negative thoughts and beliefs, the emotional wounds and resentments, the spiritual disconnection from our Source, all which can manifest as physical illness and permeate our lives in many peculiar ways.

During my first year of studies and through an experiential learning process, I developed a consistent practice to heal, activate, and nurture the development of each level.

The foundation on my spiritual level is prayer and meditation. I discovered I needed healing around prayer because lodged undetected in my belief system was a childhood perception doubtful that my prayers were heard, let alone answered. My resentment and resistance kept me separated from my Source in a way I wasn't conscious of. Healing this, I became receptive and open to a new more expansive relationship with my Creator. There are all types of ways of praying and various forms of meditation from many cultures. I love exploring new avenues to connect: guided meditations, chanting on the beach, reading a daily devotional, and, yes, prayers of gratitude. It doesn't matter what God you have, whether you're a Christian, Muslim, Buddhist, or simply find your bliss in nature. It is important to find activities that feed and nurture the soul.

My mental level requires the greatest amount of maintenance. My mind can be a dangerous place. I've constantly got to weed out

...ty, judgments, and old beliefs that no longer serve me. It's all about making a choice to change what I choose to think and believe that I have the power to do so. I actively bring statements of truth and use affirmations like *I am more than enough* and *I am perfect and whole* as a means of transforming negative thoughts and beliefs. I can also reframe my judgments by reaching for a higher perspective. My passion for writing helps stimulate my mental faculties, and I use motivational reading and conversation to keep focused on inspirational ideas. The key is consistency and a commitment to develop new perceptions while allowing the world to be a mirror.

Love, compassion, and self-forgiveness are the primary tools I use to nurture my emotional level. My heart has taken a beating in this lifetime and my choices today reflect a level of honor and self-respect. Part of my healing entails making sure the little girl inside, who was bogged down with pain and sorrow as a child, gets to experience activities that bring her joy on a regular basis: singing, strumming my guitar, ice cream, a good laugh with friends, a supportive community—all which fill me with a sense of emotional warmth and wellbeing.

In a fast paced world, it is easy to innocently abandon ourselves by charging through and dismissing our emotions. Take time out to be kind, gentle, and loving, especially in times of fear—that pesky, sometimes debilitating, emotion that keeps love thwarted and stifles power. Remember love is all that's real and, forgive, forgive, forgive.

Physical activity, eating healthy, internal cleanses, and a good night's rest all serve to maintain balance and equilibrium on my physical level. It is imperative I keep the temple that houses my Spirit in good condition. By doing so, it helps facilitate healing on all my other levels. Eating organic foods assists with mental clarity. Activities like Yoga, surfing, and jogging increase circulation, and move old energies out of making room for the new. Equally important is rest and rejuvenation which should be taken with pleasure. The body heals more rapidly during this time. One of my favorites is a candle and the scent of lavender placed by my bedside setting the stage for peaceful sleep. The possibilities to care for the physical level are endless, so be creative and make it fun.

Yes, diligence and discipline are required to dig deep and make the changes, but they're well worth it. My life today is carrying a new vibration. A new world is unfolding in front of me. By paying attention to my internal wellbeing first and foremost, manifesting what I desire comes with ease. I've continued on with Inner Visions and my spiritual development. I have a clear vision and am now consciously co-creating it. I've started a healing arts practice. And, here, I continue my passion for writing. Most importantly, I'm experiencing a new way of being—authentically and joyfully expressing all that I am. I found what I was looking for within: truly a natural high.

About the Author

Shannon is an author, healer, entrepreneur, and visionary. She nests on the Hawaiian island of Maui, where she scribed her memoir of a dark past and healing journey. Jaded Grace landed her as a finalist in the Indie Publishing Contest at the San Francisco Writers Conference and was published in 2013. As a healer, she is gifted with the ability to channel; is empathic, clairaudient, and clairsentient; and is a Reiki Practitioner and offers her services globally.

http://www.urthanjl.com

The Heart of Wellness

———— ∞ ————

Dr. Jonah Yakel

Initiation Into Love

Sweat poured down my face as I neared exhaustion. At this moment in time, it was unbelievable to think that a mere fifteen months earlier I was fighting for my life in an operating room after experiencing a devastating and near fatal car accident. My body had been completely crushed after being hit from the side by a speeding stolen car that ran a red light. In addition to more than twenty-five fractures in my body, I experienced massive internal injuries. Major organs hemorrhaged. As both lungs filled with blood and fluid my left one collapsed, both kidneys went into failure, my diaphragm was torn, and my spleen was damaged beyond repair. I spent the next month in ICU, struggling for every breath. Yet, as improbable as it sounds, here I was, fourteen months later, at the pinnacle of a 450-mile bike ride from Washington DC to New Lebanon, NY.

Four days into our bike quest, I felt incredible pain shoot through my ribs as my lungs seared with every breath, my pelvis—having been crushed in the accident—throbbed with pain from days of prolonged sitting on a bike seat, and my legs burned as I pushed my way up Storm Kill Mountain in upstate New York. Closing in on muscle failure, I settled into my breath, focusing intensely as I directed it into my heart center. It was all I had left. Moving my presence and awareness from my mind, which was on the verge of breaking due to sheer pain, into my heart I felt a shift

20

take place. My heart began to stir as I felt a warm sensation grow inside me, reminiscent of the glow of golden embers in a burning fire. This inner heat began expanding, circulating around my entire body. Determined to continue onward, I matched the rhythm of my breath to the cadence of my pedaling.

Suddenly, I was overcome with strength. I felt a raw, surging force well up within me. It was a power unlike anything I had ever experienced. I never knew such strength existed, especially within my own being. It felt as though my heart had taken over control of my body.

I stood up on the pedals and began picking up speed. Before long, I was riding up the mountain with near ease. My pain had nearly become an afterthought. After forty-five minutes of steep uphill riding, I reached the top of the mountain, feeling completely invigorated, alive, and in love. Grateful beyond words to even be alive, my heart was torn wide open and, like a raging fire, was burning with love.

My life has never been the same.

Wellness is more than just the overall state of our physical health. It's about learning to live wholeheartedly, authentically, and with purpose. We spend the majority of our days lost in our thoughts, fears, and worries, when we could instead be experiencing the remarkable love that radiates within us. The true path to wellness isn't about curing symptoms; it's a journey into our hearts. My journey has taught me quite clearly that wellness is not something we do; it's who we are. It's a state of being. As we travel from our heads to our hearts, we restore wholeness to our lives, physically, mentally, emotionally, and spiritually. Lying dormant inside us is that true catalyst for all healing and wellness: love.

For most of us, the heart is a place that we rarely seek to enter because it can be uncomfortable and because it requires a willingness to surrender and to experience our own vulnerability. To avoid this, most of us have distracted ourselves by becoming so busy and overwhelmed by our day-to-day responsibilities that we have taken up permanent residence inside our heads. We spend a large part of our waking hours consumed by worries of the future or stuck in the stories of the past. Completely caught up in *doing*, there is no time for simply *being*. This lifestyle takes a toll on us, physically and emotionally, ultimately leading us to feel overwhelmed, anxious, exhausted, and burnt out.

While we constantly seek a cure for our various symptoms, no external source will replace the work required to heal and experience wellness. The root of the pain we experience in all our various symptoms are the cries of our bodies, our hearts, our souls, yearning for connection.

Finding Your Heart

Healing requires living from the heart, which we must first learn to access. Below, I have included a practice that begins this process. The key is the breath, which, through it, we have been given the opportunity to move beyond the concepts and mental constructs of oneness, unity, and love, and to truly experience them. More so, the sacredness of our breath allows us to connect to our heart. It's only from the heart that we can experience the truth of Divine Love and our connection to the Universe and our role in its continued unfoldment. In the following practice, we use the breath to begin experiencing the heart.

1. Sitting comfortably with the spine aligned, shoulders relaxed, and eyes closed, bring your attention to your breath.

2. Feel your inhalation moving in through your nose, filling your lungs, and oxygenating every cell in your body.

3. Equally bring your awareness to your exhalation. Imagine all the leftover and used gases and toxins from your body being returned to the lungs and released through your nose into the atmosphere. This is a great time to let go of any stress and tension from your day and to abandon any thoughts and worries of the future.

4. Once you have witnessed your breath for several minutes, redirect your awareness to the area of your heart, just left of the midpoint in your chest. Feel the rhythm of your heartbeat as it brings life to every cell in your body with every pulsation. It can often be helpful to place your hand over your heart.

5. As you inhale, imagine breathing directly into your heart. Let the breath serve as a gentle breeze that slowly softens your heart and releases any tension and stress you are holding around it. As you continue this practice, you may feel a sense of tenderness, or vulnerability, as you loosen the chains that have bound your heart as a means of protection. Allow your heart to open, and take a moment to feel a sense of gratitude for whatever may be coming up.

6. Exhaling, imagine your heart center opening like the relaxing of a clenched fist or the blooming of a flower blossom. As you exhale, you may feel a sense of expansion, or peace, as your heart begins to unfold.

7. As you continue inhaling directly into your heart and exhaling, while you soften and expand with each breath, imagine you are moving your presence from inside your head to inside your heart. Spend as much time as you like residing within your heart center.

8. Slowly return to your natural breath. When you are ready, open your eyes.

This is a great practice to begin experiencing the space of the heart. Ideally, spend ten minutes in the morning upon rising, or in the evening before bed, resting in your heart. As with any practice or meditation, it's important not to maintain any expectation or to judge our experience. It is often difficult to feel the heart when we first begin this practice, but with time it becomes easier.

This is a practice we can always return to for a few breaths from time to time throughout the day to restore a sense of strength, clarity, focus, and love. When we learn to enter our hearts, we can quickly find our center and restore balance amidst the chaos of our everyday lives.

How Can We Love More?

The goal is not only to find and feel our heart, but also to become capable of living from it. From this space, it's possible to stay totally open and vulnerable while maintaining a tremendous amount of strength and love. It's from our hearts that we can awaken to our purpose in life as it pertains to the unfoldment of the Universe. Our true fulfillment in life is dependent on how we speak our truth, which is hidden in our heart. Underneath all our personas and stories about who we are lies our true essence. This essence exists as a frequency, a vibration. This vibration creates a note, or tone, that you alone add to the symphony of the Universe. This unique vibration is your gift to the world. When we access this vibration in our heart, it not only heals our own being, but it also actively participates in the healing of everyone and everything around us. This is loving service, and it all begins in the heart.

Ultimately, healing and wellness are not only about simply curing or removing physical symptoms or ailments, but are also about learning to enter into the sacred space of our heart. It is the process of living wholeheartedly. It's being vulnerable enough to open the heart and allowing yourself to be guided by it. From this space, we gain access to the unlimited flow of divine love, connection, and healing of the Universe. When we kindle the fire of love in our heart and learn to live there, we begin to recover from past traumas physically, mentally, and emotionally, healing not only ourselves, but the world around us as well. This is the heart of wellness.

About the Author

Doctor Yakel is a chiropractor and the owner of LifeGate Wholeness Center in Kansas City where he practices Flowtrition. He has walked the Sufi path for nearly twenty years, having been initiated into the Chistiyya lineage by Pir Vilayat Inayat Khan. Currently, Dr. Yakel teaches seminars helping people remember their divine nature, awaken their healing potential, and fulfill their sacred purpose. He is a proud supporter of MaxLove, helping kids thrive against cancer.

http://www.drjonahyakel.com

Saving My Skin

Radhika Naik Deshpande

According to the dictionary, "saving one's own skin" means to protect oneself from danger or difficulties, without worrying about other people. About four years ago, I saved my skin, in the most literal sense of words and in a spiritual way, too. I am grateful for the skin condition that brought about a transformation within my mind, body, and spirit. This transformation made me aware of the dangers of *thinking on auto-pilot*, showed me how to think consciously, and ended the affliction of constantly worrying about what others thought of me. However, my life before this skin-saving transformation was greatly different.

Nourished, nurtured, protected, well-cared-for, smooth sailing—that was my life for the first two and a half decades. Born of well-to-do, educated, and liberal parents, in a metropolitan city of Mumbai, India, I lead a very comfortable life, received good education, excelled in academics, and was considered a brilliant and well-behaved girl by most. And being the only child, I was the center of my parents' Universe. However, I am grateful to myself for deciding to venture out of my comfort zone, both psychologically and geographically, in order to pursue a Doctorate in science. Had I not lived away from home on my own, I would've never discovered who I truly was.

My four-year stay in the US got me much more than my Doctorate. The explorer in me greatly flourished. I experienced various cuisines, cultures, languages, places, and terrains while there. I gained some life-long friends and lost a lot of inhibitions. More importantly, I found my soul mate, or so I thought at the time. Our long distance relationship culminated into an engagement in about a year's time. After I received my Doctorate, the thirst for exploration guided me to Australia. I accepted the post of a research fellow in a reputed Australian national laboratory and flew to Sydney, where I lived and flourished further for the next three years.

I fell in love with Sydney quite instantly. I seemed to love my work, my life, and my fiancé, and everything appeared to be going wonderfully well—the way it had been for most of my life thus far. However, the Universe clearly had different plans for me. My soul was crying out for me to look at, and accept, the truth that I wasn't happy from within. I, of course, ignored the cry, gave myself loads of excuses, hoped that things would get better, and got married to my then fiancé.

Still in a long distance relationship after marriage, it became clear to me within a very short time that this relationship wasn't meant to work. I am thankful to myself that I didn't take very long to decide that I wanted to end my marriage. The details of the meltdown of this relationship are unimportant, since my focus here is on the healing that took place after that. It suffices to say that the following one and a half years were emotionally and psychologically extremely strenuous.

My professional life was flourishing, the personal one had dwindled, and my spiritual journey had begun, though I was unaware of it at the time. At home, I read books like Eckhart Tolle's *The Power of Now* and watched movies similar to *What the Bleep Do We Know?!* At work, I presented my research at various conferences within and outside of Australia. My awareness about how life and the Universe really worked was increasing day after day. The insights came, not in one grand moment of enlightenment, but in bite-sized realizations that I could digest with my mind, body, and soul.

One of the significant a-ha moments came during a train journey in New Zealand. I was on a vacation after presenting at a conference there, when I realized—or, should I say, accepted—that my life had been exactly what I had asked for, including my broken marriage. Everything, strangely, fell in place. I felt tremendous sadness and then a sense of relief and joy. If I had created "the bad" and "the ugly", I could also create "the good". Later that day, as I walked barefoot on the freshly rained-on grass, I felt one with the Universe. I had realized how it worked and the role I played in it.

The new year started with some difficulties on the professional front. After facing more than six months of bullying, unwilling to give in, I filed a complaint in the human resources department and went on a stress leave. My marriage and my stress leave ended at about the same time, and I resumed work with the determination to reboot my life. However, the reboot that happened was much more intense than I could ever imagine. The stress I had been under for the past couple of years resulted in an autoimmune condition, Pemphigus Vulgaris. The skin condition escalated rapidly all over my body, and I had to go on yet another leave to repair and recover myself physically.

While the physical symptoms were being taken care of by a wonderful doctor, the Universe decided it was time for me to heal myself of the patterns that were causing the dis-ease (yes, I have consciously written the word this way) in my body. An aunt gifted me a book *You Can Heal Your Life* by Louise Hay. I had never heard of her before, although I had frequented the self-help aisle of bookstores for over a year. In retrospect, I feel this was a matter of "When the student is ready, the teacher appears."

I started reading the book, and I couldn't put it down! Everything Louise said resonated deeply with me. I could see the mental patterns running the lives of people around me and my own. The matches between the specific beliefs in "the list" at the end of the book and the dis-ease were perfect in my own case and in the case of some of my family. According to Louise, disease is really a lack of ease in some way in our body—hence, dis-ease. The book stoked my appetite to know more about her philosophy. I bought *You Can Heal Your Life* the movie and watched it every single day for about three to four months! I immersed myself in her philosophy and worked on clearing my emotional patterns very sincerely.

What resulted was a miracle, in my opinion.

I was able, for the first time in my life, to accept and love myself exactly as I was. At that time, "exactly as I was" meant open skin-lesions all over my body, baldness in a couple of spots, a swollen-looking face, and a fat body due to the steroids that were given to cure my autoimmune condition. Not a very pretty visual, to say the least, to look in a mirror and say, "I love you, Radhika. I really love you!" However, that was the miracle—I was able to say it and, more importantly, feel it.

I was cured of the autoimmune condition within a couple of months and free of all medication in a year. More significantly, my emotional and psychological autoimmune condition—the self-attacking, self-criticizing nature—was cured with a generous dose of Louise's philosophy. In the following couple of years, I bought many of her books, DVDs, and also those from numerous other spiritual masters. While all the other works I came across before Louise told me about how life worked, she made it possible for me to practice those principles and transform my life.

As much as these spiritual principles support us in creating a life of our dreams, more importantly, they support us in sailing through the most difficult times of our lives. The focus of popular media is usually on the former. However, I am more grateful for the latter. The knowing that the Universe always takes care of me was what enabled me to pass through the traumatic times before, during, and after the pre-term birth of my daughter. The same knowing has given me the strength to change my career path from a scientist to a spiritual workshop leader, although almost everyone around me believes that it is a mistake.

Most of us believe that spiritual awakening happens in one grand moment of enlightenment, when all the knowing in the Universe is simply *downloaded* into us. That may be the way it happens to some. However, that is certainly not the only way. The Universe will give us the knowing in the quantum we can handle, and that is different for each one of us. It comes packaged differently for each one, too. It may be a person, a place, a thing, or simply a stream of consciousness. So walk your own path, and do not compare yours with others'.

I am forever indebted to the Universe for choosing me to walk the path that I am on, that is my life. With the intention of sharing my knowing and knowledge with others, I have become a licensed and certified Heal Your Life® workshop leader. I now offer workshops based on the philosophies that made me who I am today and wish to support as many as I can to transform their lives, the way I could.

About the Author

Radhika Naik Deshpande has a Doctorate in nuclear chemistry and has worked as a scientist for the Australian Government. A transformation in her personal and spiritual life inspired her to become a Heal Your Life® workshop leader, licensed and certified by Hay House, USA. Radhika founded Radiance Coaching with an intention of sharing the life-transforming philosophy of Louise Hay with the world. She is deeply passionate about the union of science and spirituality.

http://www.radiance-coaching.com

Life After Incest:
A Testimony to Wellness
After a Traumatic Experience

Ilse De Kegel-Van de Wiele

"Home is where your heart lies, not your furniture."

B ut what if it has been made impossible for one to feel at home anywhere, from a very young age? If one only had furniture indicating where "home" should be, while one's heart was not really wanting to be there?

For a long time, I experienced that. I was not able to feel at home anywhere.

Ever since an early age, because of not wanting to experience pain, fear, guilt, dirtiness, and everything else connected with an incestuous relationship with my father, I tried to escape. I left "my other me" behind to take it all, while hiding myself quietly into my own little world. . . .

At school, I often appeared quiet and introverted throughout my early childhood. To most of my family and acquaintances, I probably came across as a "good" girl; to some, I was the clown of the family. Most of the time, I was trying to make others laugh. Other times, I would just keep a low profile, while carefully observing other people and copying their behavior just to enable myself to fit in. I was cautious all the time. At school, I was bullied until I was twelve. Then, sadly, I myself started bullying two girls in particular. To this day, I wish I could turn back the time and undo this. . . .

Some were silently wondering what was behind this big wall of mine; others outright neglected me. I preferred the latter. My very lonely, early life was built around making absolutely sure I appeared to fit in with the herd, so no one, myself included, came close to finding my "big secret", which I once believed to be proof I must be the devil impersonated.

In my late teens, something drastically changed. I found no real happiness in being a sheep. I became a rebel. I started to eat very unhealthily and regularly drank too much. I fled into emotional eating for comfort because I wasn't getting any comfort out of living with myself.

Then, about seven years ago, memories started to creep back in. As long as I tried to negate what I knew had happened, my life, in many aspects, went further down the chute. I was divorced, lost my job twice, was left with virtually no finances, and found myself alone again. On top of that, I started to get all kinds of physical ailments, while gaining weight at the drop of a hat. A total contrast to my skinny former life.

True Wellness

Wellness, I believe, is an active process of becoming aware of and making choices toward a healthy and fulfilling life in all aspects. I had to learn the hard way that this meant taking your health and life in your own hands, not going along with the crowd, and no longer lying to yourself.

Wellness is a verb, an action, a passion.

My true path to wellness started the moment I really became honest with myself and started to accept and confront what really occurred.

So, is wellness, in all aspects of life, possible after any trauma containing one or more extremely stressful events that shatter one's sense of security, making one feel lonely, helpless, and vulnerable in a seemingly dangerous world?

I believe it is.

One does have to confront and deal with all the emotions connected. In my case, of wanting to be loved, of hanging onto those brief moments, I erroneously believed to be "love". Of being terrified of what would happen next. Of being found out. Of not being liked anymore. Feelings of sadness and pain. Feeling one is cheating on oneself and others. At one point, it becomes too much to bear for anyone, especially a young child in full development. It was at that point that I created "my other me". After that, I tried to make myself forget anything had ever happened. Until I was thirty-six, I managed to not remember anything.

But as these things have a tendency to do, they catch up with one sooner or later.

I became depressed for three years straight. Nothing seemed to help. My comfort eating habits intensified and worsened. I considered using drugs to ease off the continuous stress, frustration, and pain.

I was even on the verge of committing suicide.

I simply didn't know who I was anymore.

The Road Back

For a while, after the memories started to come back, I felt in total disbelief, like all of this could not have happened. For, if it did, surely I would have remembered something in all those years.

Next, for some time, I felt like a victim, like I had no control over things—and they kept on happening to me.

Hard as it was, I had to move out of this state of mind into a more positive one to be able to attract the right people who could help me through my "rough patches". In case anyone wonders, this was not a walk in the park.

Luckily, I attracted some very kind people and great counseling, both of which helped me create a safe space where I could finally allow myself to turn hate into gratefulness, shame into recognition, and fear into hope.

I truly peeled away all the junk and garbage surrounding me layer by layer and saw, for the first time ever, who I really am. I regained confidence and strength.

Where I had been admiring certain qualities in others before, wishing I had these too, I discovered I already had them in me . . . previously hidden.

Through all my experiences and the rough ride back to happiness, I had gained a high degree of courage to carry through any difficulties, against all odds.

Next, I turned my bitterness into gratitude and my hate and hard feelings into passion with a burning desire to help.

Happiness

I am finally making peace with the demons of my past, able to live fully in the present, with a healthy interest in creating a great future.

I am truly grateful for attracting a lovely husband, who deserves a medal for sticking with me throughout the past few years, despite some of my emotional flare-ups. I absolutely love our two wonderful children, who, in their youth, purity, and high interest in their surrounds, inspire me into being a good example for them, every day a little better. I have a great job and lovely colleagues.

I am a strong believer in the fact that true gratitude is one of the main qualities that can turn one into a magnet for good things. As long as I have been applying this, great opportunities have come my way on a regular basis.

I know I still have some work to do in my quest for total happiness. There are still some old "bad" habits I want to revert into "good" ones.

Slowly but surely I am starting to manifest the life I love, physically, mentally, and spiritually. I have no more physical trouble, no signs of depression, and I keep my weight at a level I like, without any diet. I am feeling full of life, passion, and energy again. Accepting what had happened was one of the hardest things in my life, after experiencing it, yet sharing my experience, in order to help others, is the next step toward true healing.

I find that my own experiences have enabled me to really understand what others are going through, no matter the trauma. I know each of us have our own, sometimes unknowingly leading us astray into a world of negativity. Having come this far, I can now help others achieve their goals to finally live life as they want it, through laser precise nutrition testing and gentle coaching.

Helping others had always been my driving force. It's what made me become a volunteer from the age of fourteen, and more recently a health coach and author. I have a strong desire to help other parents and their children take charge again of their own life and health in a harmonic and informed way. I love seeing those who were previously without hope, after years of searching everywhere for solutions, getting back sparks of hope in their eyes, as they see things turn around. I love helping others create the life they love.

Wish

As I mentioned before, writing this down has been extremely hard and personal for me. But even if only one person who once was silenced gets inspired by my story, finds his or her voice back, and starts on the road back, that makes it worth it. There's no need to carry such a burden alone. There is a way out, there is hope for those who want to heal. All can be helped.

So, in the future if you see someone shying away, behaving strange in any way, or trying to get you off of their back when you try to help them, please just realize they might not want it that way. Maybe they actually want to be helped but are too scared to ask. Maybe all they want is a hug, when all they seem to do is bite at you. . . .

Please, hold out your hand for however long it takes. When they do take it, they have reached the first step toward wanting to heal. At that point, they will be very grateful you persisted.

About the Author

Ilse Van de Wiele is a certified holistic health coach, specialized in helping to relieve any acute and chronic discomforts through a healthy lifestyle, laser precise nutritional testing, and natural supplements.

Her passion is in helping conscious parents age gracefully while providing a healthy foundation for their children.

She is a blogger, co-author in the bestselling *Adventures in Manifesting* series, and part of the advisory board of the National Health Federation.

http://www.consciously-in-balance.com

How Love Can Change Your Life

———— ∞∞∞ ————

Catherine Robertson

Two years ago, if anyone had looked closely they would have seen what many would call the perfect life. I had a fabulous job, which brought me security and success, a kind-hearted and beautifully natured daughter, a stable marriage to a patient and loyal husband, perfect health, a busy social life, and some money in the bank.

There was nothing "wrong" with me; but, when I look back now, I can recognize how detached I was from my true self and how much joy had vanished from my heart and soul. It felt like a low grade discontent that was always present in the background of my mind, and would occasionally raise its voice as if to say, "Is this all there is to life?" It sucked my energy a lot more than I realized, but whenever the discomfort got too great, I rationalized it by telling myself that this was the life that I had chosen, that there were a lot of people out there who were worse off than me, and that I should just suck it up and get on with things!

I had developed a mindset over the years that had pretty strong martyr-like tendencies. And, as life decided to throw various crises towards my husband and I, pretty much one after another, I took on the burden of responsibility of holding work and family life together—all the while trying to fix and rescue those around me, failing to realize that it was all irrelevant, as the one I needed to fix and rescue was myself. Everything in my life had been merely a smokescreen for disguising my own pain, and I had done a good job of distracting myself from that pain for a really long time.

So I got on with dealing with the demands of everyday life and kept busy enough that I didn't have time to think about the discontent too deeply or listen to that nagging voice in the back of my head too often. But that level of denial and distraction can only last for so long, and I now realize that if we don't listen to the voice inside of us and start making some changes in our lives, then the Universe will give us an almighty wake up call to shake us out of our fog.

That was exactly what happened to me in December 2012.

It was around that time that my father in law, who had been battling an aggressive cancer and with whom I shared a close bond, had an unexpected seizure. The suddenness of the seizure, at a time when he had been relatively stable, shocked our whole family and left me feeling completely and utterly broken.

I was a mess.

However, despite the level of pain that I was in, I viewed it as just another crisis that we would have to get through, and so I kept going and tried to hold it all together—working, caring for my family, and being the martyr I was always used to being. That was until my manager stepped in and told me in no uncertain terms to stop work immediately and to go and spend time with my family. He also very kindly and gently suggested that I wasn't coping with the current circumstances and would possibly benefit from receiving some counseling.

I believe he was sent to deliver an important message to me, almost like an angel in disguise, as it was at exactly that moment that my intuition woke up—and, for the first time, I started to listen and to follow it. I recall feeling with absolute certainty that counseling wouldn't be enough to tackle the pain that I was currently experiencing, and that I needed something more, something deeper. I also knew on some level that what I was feeling wasn't simply the impending loss of someone I loved dearly. I needed to wake up!

Now, at that point, I had no idea what waking up meant, and the whole concept of spiritual growth, being fully conscious, and even the Law of Attraction meant nothing to me. But, looking back, I do believe that I was being guided toward this area, and I suddenly remembered a friend talking about Kinesiology and how much it had helped her. I didn't know much about it, but recalled her explaining how the therapist was able to locate a deeply hidden memory and trauma in her subconscious, which had then manifested as a physical illness. Through identifying this blockage, the trauma was released and the physical illness resolved.

So I began a trawl of the internet, reading the profiles and websites of dozens of holistic therapists, until I found my second angel, who would facilitate my healing journey and help me turn my life around. This wonderful healer quickly went to work on my broken and wounded spirit and set about helping me remove all of the self-limiting beliefs and programs that I had been living with and that had been holding me back from reaching my full potential.

The first effect I noticed was that it was as if someone had turned down the volume in my head, and the constant chatter became quieter. With each session, I could feel myself becoming lighter, having more energy, and experiencing sudden insights and clarity about why I had behaved and reacted to events in the past in a specific way.

There were times when this work was incredibly painful and emotional; however, as each layer was peeled away to reveal more of my true and authentic self, I became happier and more settled in my own skin, which felt amazing! As I became freer and lighter, friends and family started to notice that I "seemed different" and that my old, reactive personality was replaced with an inner peace and calm, which had clearly become visible.

The development of awareness, while wonderful and liberating, brings with it a big responsibility, and that responsibility means that it no longer becomes possible to lie to yourself. When pains and hurts that were once buried deep within your subconscious come to light, there is then a duty to pay attention and act on them, and this is where the role of courage steps onto the path to wellness.

For me, the major realization was when I acknowledged and dealt with the insight that my husband and I had reached the end of our journey together and that our marriage was sadly over. While this realization was enormously painful and led to many "dark nights of the soul", before I was able to articulate my decision, the sense of peace that came over me when we shared our truth with each other was profound, and that peace has been with me ever since.

Since I've been able to connect to my heart and truth in this way, and to take that leap of faith, I've discovered that life and how the world responds to me has completely transformed. Being truly authentic and feeling what life really wants me to experience, both the happy and the sad, has allowed my life to blossom and flow effortlessly. The love that I've found for myself has released an inner peace and contentment that is now unshakable, and the Universe has rewarded me by sending that love back tenfold. I've realized how magical and fun this game of life can be through the constant cycle of sending out love and gratitude to the world and by allowing yourself to receive abundance and blessings from the Universe in return.

Today, I have clarity. I follow my intuition and listen to my heart, and I have found a deep sense of happiness and peace that I never knew existed before. Some days I feel the joy bursting out of every cell in my body and catch myself grinning like a maniac, causing me to cry with absolute gratitude at just how good I feel!

And I want everyone to feel this good—there is no reason why we all shouldn't. It's our absolute right to live in a state of complete love and happiness, and by participating in this wonderful book I'm proof that the path to wellness is real and achievable for everyone. Don't wait like I did for a crisis to hit. If you have that nagging voice in the back of your head, if you feel the urge to find your purpose in life, if you ever think "Is this all there is?" then, please, take the leap, face your fears, and begin your own journey of discovery. I promise that you will find your wings, and your life will begin to unfold like magic.

You don't need to be afraid. Know that whatever pain you feel won't last forever, that the lightness is there waiting for you, and that when you reach it you will be completely transformed. Love and happiness will fill your heart and soul, and life will be more amazing and beautiful than you ever believed possible.

Just take that first step, make a decision that you want more from your life, and follow your heart. It knows what to do.

About the Author

Catherine Robertson is an intuitive energy healer with a passion for inspiring others to begin their own healing journey of transformation. She has a natural talent for communication and for finding an authentic point of connection with everyone she meets, and she has a deep love of all matters metaphysical. Her life purpose is to assist in facilitating the journey of awakening and self-healing for all those who are ready to step into the light.

http://www.catherinerobertson.org

Light Up Your Life With the Universe

Adrian Ng

The Universe we live in is truly complex and amazing. More and more people are experiencing life-changing events of a spiritual nature with the Universe's help that often defy conventional logic and possibilities. Through such powerful transformational experiences, their lives totally light up and get filled with joy, abundance, and wellness.

Mine is one of those stories.

I grew up in a traditional Asian family that believes strongly in following the conventional crowd and places extreme importance on being able to earn a proper living at the expense of happiness and love. My parents had a serious case of "scarcity consciousness" because they grew up in families that had suffered tremendously during and after World War II. Being so used to experiencing a constant lack of money to afford many things when they were young, my parents continued to place matters of practicality above all else.

They brought their negative emotional and mental baggage from their unhappy and deprived childhood into our family. Sounds of laughter and joy were seldom heard of in my home. My father did not earn much money, and my mother was a housewife. Quarrels over money happened often.

While I was young, I had often envied my friends who had loving families that had much love and joy. I often asked myself,

"Why can't I have a family like them?" Yet, that was a question I had no answers for. All I could do was press on and do whatever I could on my own. As my friends received positive and loving words of encouragement or advice from their parents when they encountered difficulties, I grew up with no emotional support from my parents. I often had to find the emotional strength from within myself when faced with personal matters that troubled me throughout my growing up years, such as issues involving relationships, studies, or career.

My family background had long closed my heart to life matters. Making more money was always on my mind, as I did not want to go through financial hardship anymore. I started my career in the technology industry but quickly moved onto the banking one, which paid much more. During the early years of my career, a psychic told me that I have many important things to do in my life and that I am supposed to be a spiritual healer/teacher and help transform the lives of people around the world. However, I felt that it was not a viable career, and my parents would be strongly opposed to it, even though I would have loved doing it. Putting that idea at the back of my mind, I focused on my corporate career and progressed to the level of vice president in a large regional bank in Singapore.

That was when my life took a drastic plunge toward darkness. I became obsessed with making quick money. I left my banking job and became a day trader dealing with the stock market. I was creating substantial wealth on a daily basis, and the constant adrenaline rush and greed of making quick money completely overwhelmed me. My risk appetite was fast growing to a dangerous level. The Universe, through my Spirit Guide, then warned me to "be careful", but my negative state of mind then would not listen. I was trading with huge sums of money on credit, in the hope of growing my wealth in the shortest time possible.

My good run on the stock market had ended. It became a period of daily losses, one after another. Desperate to overturn my huge losses, I used more money on credit to trade even more aggressively, hoping that the profit from one good trade would completely clear all my debts. But that was purely wishful thinking. As a result, I ended up not only losing all my hard-earned savings, but also incurring a very significant six-digit debt.

At that point, I no longer had a job, so I did not have any income. My parents did not have the money to help me, and I could not tell them about my financial problems. Even during normal times, they were constantly worrying about not having enough money. Imagine what the shock of my huge debts would do if they knew! I felt I could not bring more worries to them, and it would cause irreversible damage to our relationship. I could not approach my friends for help either, as I did not know how or when I could repay them. I did not want the issue of money to spoil my friendships built over the years. Besides, they needed money for their own family commitments.

My romantic relationship was next in line to suffer. My girlfriend then was under the severe stress of not knowing the future of our relationship. Without a job and without the means to clear my huge debts, and no longer having the ability to save up for marriage, the future of our relationship was completely bleak. As much as she could help me, my financial issues were simply too great for me to handle. In the end, we both arrived at the inevitable and painful decision to end our relationship. I could not hold back her life anymore because of my problems, as she very much wanted to get married and have a family soon.

I felt my life had truly plunged to the depths of Hell, as everything in my life had collapsed on me. I felt so alone, afraid, and helpless. I did not want to get out of bed, as there was nothing I could look forward to every day, and nothing I could do to improve my dire situation. The persistent thoughts of my problems, my mistakes, and my negative decisions over the years kept running endlessly in my mind. I cried whenever I thought of how my greed and folly had thrown my relationship and future away. I wished with all my heart that I could turn back the clock to the time before all my problems started.

But of course, that was impossible.

Though I had already known many years ago what my life purpose was, I had never truly spent enough time and effort making it happen. Given my hopeless state then, fulfilling my life purpose seemed to be nowhere within my reach. The significant monthly interest payments that I could not afford to pay, plus the fact that I had no job, with no more savings to draw upon, with no one to help me, made my life situation beyond remedy.

I was already in a deep state of depression, and for a few days in a row, before I went to bed, I told God/Source, "I can't continue with my life anymore, as I have no way to solve my problems. I know what my life purpose is, but I give up. Just take me back, so I do not wake up tomorrow."

Some days later, God/Source wanted me to confirm my request to end my life. By then, I had calmed down slightly and told God/Source that I had changed my mind and wished to continue my life to fulfill my purpose, but I needed the Universe's help with my massive problems, as I could not solve them on my own.

After passing through that "dark night of the soul", and completely letting go of my negativity, I experienced three weeks of total peace and bliss, as if time stood still. Then, my life quickly rose up from the depths of darkness. I began to live and flow with the rhythm of the Universe. My psychic, spiritual, and healing abilities were enhanced significantly, and I was able to receive clear guidance from the Universe to help me successfully overcome my problems. The raw land investments that I was stuck with for seven years miraculously attracted a buyer, and it helped me receive a substantial sum of money to help me with my debts.

As I was finally ready to focus my mind and heart on fulfilling my life purpose as a spiritual healer/teacher, the Universe further guided me to advance my healing certifications and skills. Following that, many people from around the world were guided by the Universe to find me to help them with various difficult health, life, and spiritual issues. My business of providing healing, life guidance, and psychic and spiritual services was finally blossoming with the Universe's help, and gave me the abundance to clear my remaining debts. My relationship with my parents also improved tremendously, as they became more open to the Universe's role in our lives, after seeing how I am able to help so many people with my successful business.

The unbearable suffering that I had experienced over the years provided me with the opportunity to truly let go of my old self that was consumed with negativity and to transform both myself and my life completely. It helped me understand people's suffering and life problems much more deeply so that I could help them effectively. Being able to fulfill my meaningful life purpose while leading a life of abundance gives me great joy, which I truly hope everyone can experience.

Everyone deserves to be happy and live well, regardless of their life's circumstances. If you are open to receiving the Universe's guidance and help, you will receive it and it will light up your life, as long as you are willing to let go of your negativity and learn to be a much more positive person.

About the Author

Adrian Ng is a naturally gifted psychic and healer. He is highly sought after worldwide for his powerful and effective healing and spiritual abilities. He provides holistic and non-religious healing and life guidance services with the help of the Universe (God/ Source, Ascended Masters and Archangels, Spirit Guides and Higher Selves of his clients). He also teaches people how to improve their health and lives, as well as about spiritual advancement.

http://www.livinglightuniverse.com

Adversity is an Opportunity for Life-Changing Transformation

Bob Doyle

I was stressed, angry, exhausted, and broke. Depression and anxiety attacks were the way I started *every* day. I'd lost my marriage, my home, my dogs, and virtually every penny I'd ever saved and invested. I couldn't sleep, and I didn't exercise. Almost my whole life had become about putting out one fire after another and, somehow, trying to keep my head above water.

It was the most hopeless I'd ever felt.

The real kicker is that all this was happening not that long ago . . . and just a few years after my appearance in the film *The Secret*, as an expert in teaching people the Law of Attraction—in essence, the science of living your life by design, filled with passion and abundance.

So what happened? And where was the Law of Attraction when *I* needed it? How did I attract this series of apparent catastrophes, and why couldn't I just attract something else?

Adversity can happen to anyone, and at any time. However, human beings have an enormous power to transcend adversity whenever it occurs and to create something entirely new as a result—something better than they ever could have imagined. However, the fact is, most people don't know that—and even if they *do* know, it's very easy to disregard it when they're consumed with all the negativity associated with the experience.

The truth is, we're actually making a choice—however subconscious it is—to hang on to the negative feelings, even though it doesn't always feel like a choice. But the fact is that, at any time, we do have the ability to shift our attention to thoughts that create positive feelings.

Yet, we so often continue to wallow in our misery.

In my case, this is exactly what I was doing. I carried a tremendous amount of guilt related to many aspects of leaving a twenty-four-year marriage. I knew, for example, decades before I actually left the marriage that I did not need to be married and could not bring to the relationship what was necessary to sustain passion, intimacy, and connectedness. The reasons for that is another story entirely, but the point is that I spent years feeling guilty for the misery I was causing my entire family—because I was dominated by fear and because I was unable to take the action I finally ended up taking.

As a result, when I did leave, it was exponentially worse than it needed to be. The pain my action caused to my ex-wife, children, and friends created feelings of guilt unlike anything I'd ever experienced. I went through frequent feelings of hating myself. Most importantly, *I felt I deserved the adversity.*

We all have our reasons for holding on to negative feelings for too long and for creating extended periods of adversity. The only thing that matters is what choices we make about what we're experiencing.

Because I teach the Law of Attraction, I need to point out that where we choose to put our attention and how we choose to emotionally interpret our circumstances make all the difference in terms of how long we stay in adversity and how "bad" it gets.

Unfortunately, in these situations, we are consumed by the perceived problem and all we want to do is solve it. The problem is that when we are focused on, and really feeling and experiencing the negativity associated with, the problem, we are actually attracting more of it. There is actually physics behind this; but, regardless, it just makes sense that if we are continually in a negative state, or operating from fear, we would be unable to think creatively and resourcefully. All we want is the quickest fix possible, and we are hoping, ironically, to be able to come up with the solution to all our problems when our mind is probably at its most ineffective.

What happened in my case, even before my eventual divorce, and what actually started my own downward spiral, is that I lost my vision. And in such circumstances, only a powerful vision will change your circumstances.

What I didn't mention is that during the time period I described at the beginning of this chapter, I also happened to be living in a veritable paradise (and still do) with the absolute love of my life. By all rights, I should have been ridiculously happy. I always told myself (which is way different than "believing") that when I was able to move through the fear of leaving what I perceived as a highly destructive relationship with my ex-wife, *everything* was going to instantly fall into place.

I told myself that my business would instantly start rocking again and that all the heaviness that I'd been carrying would just instantly dissolve. I had not anticipated just how significant the emotional and financial post-divorce fallout would affect my spirit. And when leaving the marriage did *not* instantly "solve all my problems", I was even more disheartened.

Was all this pain for nothing? I mean, here I was, living in a beautiful home by the water, with an amazing woman who stuck by me and supported me even in my darkest moments. Yet I was, somehow, unable to sustain a sense of gratitude for that?

Without even realizing it, my self-talk was all about survival— about just making it through another day.

I had once again lost so much of my vision for I had such a powerful conversation running: "I don't deserve what I want because I hurt my family." Everything became about managing the chaos I had created as I let my emotions get out of control during the stress and trauma of my divorce.

Old beliefs from my youth about "anything good I receive will be taken away" had saturated my very being. I really had no idea how out of control it had gotten . . . until my very own daughter, after visiting with us for a few days, said to me, "You know, your conversations all have a theme of 'just making it' and 'keeping your head above water'."

She didn't have to say another word. I just let that sink in, and I was able to see in mere moments just what I'd done to myself. More importantly, what I needed to do to change it.

First, I had to make a decision that I was done wallowing in my adversity. I'd perpetuated my situation far longer than I needed to, and taking responsibility for that was going to be key. I can't blame the divorce, my ex, the economy, or *anyone*.

I also immediately created an audio recording of affirmations for myself. This is a basic exercise that I had, somehow, moved away from. So making this recording and listening to it daily was very empowering, and I was able to feel things shifting almost immediately.

I made a vision board that inspired me. Basically, I went back to my "Law of Attraction roots". Instead of hiding from people while I tried to "fix all my problems", I found a way to tap into my desire to contribute to others, which I started doing. In essence, I allowed my true nature to flow from me not only with the intention of contributing to others, but also to connecting with them on a whole new level.

I re-engaged with the students who had benefitted from my work, and, almost immediately, my sense of self-worth was back in place.

Basically, I had to completely let go of my "story" about being bad, wrong, selfish, and any number of other adjectives that in no way served me. I had to be willing to re-accept my own power, value, and ability to powerfully and positively impact the world just by being exactly who I am, regardless of what others may be feeling about me.

As soon as I did this, everything changed.

I started riding my bike (along the ocean I might add—something that was always available to me, but I was so "in my stuff", I didn't make the time). I started kayaking and stand-up paddle boarding. I began playing more music again, honoring my creative nature. Basically, I was saying thank you to all that I had attracted instead of finding reasons to why I didn't deserve it.

As far as money went . . . well, as soon as I let go of trying to "fix what was broken" and totally opened myself up to abundance in any form, the most amazing opportunities and people showed up in my space, and I will truly never have to worry about money again. I also won't have to work extra hard to have it continuously flow. Had I not let go of all the self-loathing conversations, that opportunity may have never occurred.

Temporary adversity is not always a choice; extended adversity almost always is.

Adversity is an opportunity for course correction. A sign from the Universe that it may be time for an energetic realignment. A time to shift your attention from your problems to your most inspired vision.

We have the ability to say yes or no to creating something extraordinary out of adversity, and we are inspired by stories all the time of people saying yes and changing not only their own lives, but also the lives of others.

So when adversity shows up, take a bird's eye view of the situation and recognize it for what it is: temporary—unless you *decide* otherwise.

We as humans are truly powerful "reality creators". We're creating all the time. The more conscious we become of that, the richer our life experience can be . . . adversity and all.

About the Author

Bob Doyle is the bestselling author of *Follow Your Passion, Find Your Power* and one of the featured teachers in the film and book *The Secret*.

His approach to teaching the Law of Attraction is based on science and its practical implementation into everyday life. His *Wealth Beyond Reason* program is widely considered to be among the most comprehensive curriculum on the Law of Attraction available.

http://www.wealthbeyondreason.com

Falling Into the
Garden of Healing

———— ∞∞∞ ————

Debbie Engelmann

Not all gifts are appealing when first received. My gift from the Universe appeared in the form of death. Not just once, but twice. My painful journey began when my only siblings, two sisters, transitioned five months apart. Their passing pushed me—no, actually, *shoved* me—into an undulating downward spiral where time no longer seemed to have meaning. I kept falling until even the darkness itself no longer seemed to exist.

All was simply a vacuum of nothingness.

Eventually, I became cognizant of a soft supportive pillow beneath me. I had landed on what seemed to be a dimly lit desert oasis that brightened as I slowly became conscious. Through my healing, the oasis evolved into an incredible garden, literally and figuratively. It was watered by my tears, grew beautiful flowers full of vibrant colors that ushered in the new thoughts, possibilities, loving memories, and eventually peace for all that had come before. Slowly, the illusions that hid and festered in my mind and heart began to fall away. While building my sacred garden through conscious healing, the new me met the old me; we hugged and became one. The true gift *was* the experience of their deaths.

Each sister was very different and unique. One experienced life with a positive, loving outlook and chose to flow through painful events by learning from them and making the best of difficult situations. The other held the hurts of childhood close to her heart and shielded herself by reacting to life events with resistance and continual attempts to control the uncontrollable. She spent her time trying not to be hurt. As they walked their personal path toward transition, their journeys actually mimicked how they viewed and lived their lives. The first survived more than a year longer than the doctors had thought possible with grace and hope. The second passed within five months of diagnosis.

While I pondered the difference between the two, the mind-body connection became very clear to me. What we feel emotionally on a conscious and sub-conscious level affects every cell of our body. We carry lots of baggage in our hearts and minds, and it impacts all aspects of health. One sister focused on positive outcomes; the other needed to stay in victimhood. The latter suffered much more than the first. When I examined myself, I discovered I was more like my second sister. My soul was full of the effects abuse creates in a mind, body, and spirit.

The process of my healing was painful in all aspects of my human self and my soul. Not only was it necessary to grapple with the physical absence of my sisters, but I also needed to come to terms with the fact that my entire birth family was gone except me. I was alone—an orphan. The whole of me reacted to the injustice of my loss by also exposing all my buried negative energy and pain regarding my own personal abuse story. Now, every bit of me was completely consumed by negative emotion as I attempted to destroy the feelings.

This intense grief and anger, coupled with my futile attempts to stuff all feelings, created a need in me to verbally express to everyone the pure hatred I felt toward basically everything and anything. Understandably, I was disintegrating inside. My rage was on a rampage, and my body continually went out of balance. Within the first two years, I was hospitalized over twelve times with asthma: a condition I had from childhood that generally only impacted me with chest colds.

During my healing process, I learned to focus completely on myself, began to cautiously face the truth of me, and began to slowly release myself from my self-imposed cage of fear. The time estimates of others regarding how long I should grieve were finally ignored. By allowing myself to *lose control*, I began to stop controlling myself and others. I screamed; hit pillows; wrote pages and pages of memories, hatred, sadness, and unspeakable things; and when I was finally spent, it was upon Mother Earth I fell to surrender my grief and pain.

It was through the experiences of walking each sister to the grave and of my own healing journey that I heart-breakingly noticed the tendency many of us carry within to go through our daily lives, responding to the outer-world *only*. We experience infinite thoughts regarding how we *think* our physical body feels, what emotions we *think* we should be experiencing, and who the person we project *should* be. Our thoughts are full of mind-chatter, stored hurts, and the constant battle to differentiate between what is real and illusion. What stands out the most is the amazing skill we develop to avoid showing any part of our true *self*. What we project to the world is basically a self-preservation illusion of a story our mind creates. Stories that are far from the truth of who we are. Each of us is a unique energy within this universe—one of a kind. All choices, whether conscious or unconscious, equally impact all aspects of our body, emotions, and spirit, and create an ever expanding ripple of "cause and effect" that expands without limits.

As I slowly pulled myself out of victimhood, my new life evolved. I gradually completed the educational portions of my training in natural health, traditional naturopathy, and herbalism. The people who loved and supported me, my life style changes, the energy healings and healers, and especially the stillness of meditation were all major parts of rebuilding my foundation to allow my soul to finally *receive* love.

While working in a cancer center, it became very clear to me that healing, whether it is palliative in nature or simply to achieve the best possible state of health during illness, is accomplished by healing the exact same parts of our human and energetic existence. The mental cognitive state, the condition of the physical body, the strength of spirituality in whatever form is appropriate for that person, and most importantly the health of our soul condition (or conditioning) must all be touched, loved, and healed. The power to heal is available to all of us in every moment of our existence.

In the natural healing world, scientists believe our physical bodies are about six months behind real-time and complete healing takes a minimum of two months for every year of "acquiring" an imbalance. Quickly painting over a water stain on a wall allows the stain to eventually work its way through the paint again. That happens in the physical body as well. Emotional pain, anger, fatigue, and lack of self-care all lead to physical manifestations of disease *designed* to get our attention. When disease shows up, we need to inspect all parts of our life with objective compassion and understanding to discover what may have gone out of balance so healing can begin. Healing is not an instant accomplishment. It can't be.

Any path we choose to walk is basically a guideline showing us where one *may* walk, but each step taken on that path is unique to the walker. It is *impossible* to heal the body without facing who we truly are. We are not an extension of others; we are ourselves. As we heal and release the old, more and more of the beautiful soul uniquely ours merges with our physical body. Communication between all parts of who we are becomes more fluid and natural. By healing all parts of us together, like "sisters", we move toward balanced wellness. That is true lasting healing—the completion of a circular process that involves every single part of who we are. True healing cannot be attained in singularity. That is what I personally experienced and continually see happening in my practice.

I believe we need to frequently monitor the beliefs buried deep in our spiritual structure by examining them along with the contents of our mental/logical and emotional/feeling filing cabinets. We can simply notice how they affect us and then decide if they still serve us. If we need to discard something that no longer serves us, such as emotional wounds, physical hurts, and especially words spoken that spear us like a harpoon with a cord continually pulling our heart-strings, they can safely be thrown into the wind with our blessings without judgment of self or others. The more we toss, the more genuine we become.

Thankfully, the goals I came into this life with were stronger than my grief. Through embracing personal devastation and healing myself, I became a healer. That was my true education. No big surprise really. The old must go for the new to move in. Now I plant, redesign, weed, and nourish my garden as I continue to walk the path of this life. Most of my days are experienced with silly childish fascination and excitement for the simplest things. I'm in a place where compassion and connection to everything in this universe becomes part of my soul and humanness. I realize that every thought and action we create during our time on Earth affects not only each of us, but the entire universe as well. We are *all* co-creators of everything that is.

Our own greatest mystery is to solve ourselves and heal. We tend not to see things as they are; we see them as *we* are. It is obvious that it was me who was blessed through this painful process of falling into the Garden of Healing. There is no absolute *good* or *bad* in our world; *pure love* can be found beneath both. The challenge is to allow ourselves to be loved, especially by our *self*. Why do so many people cross our path? Because without them, we would never see ourselves. And I know without a doubt that every person I encounter may sometimes be my student.

But most of the time they are my teachers.

About the Author

Debbie Engelmann holds a Doctoral Degree in natural health and traditional naturopathy and is an herbal practitioner. Through her personal and professional experience, she designed a unique method of empowering individuals to use their inherent healing ability to release negative belief patterns and achieve their highest natural level of balance and vibrancy. *Created by Nature Wellness* was designed using elements of her personal healing and the discovery that solitude is a human presumption, not reality.

http://www.createdbynaturewellness.com

Be Open to Your Higher Power

Dee Dee Delkamp

S ometimes, we experience events in our lives that, at the time, seem inconvenient, stressful, or even crippling. We become too preoccupied or traumatized by the situation to see the reasons, lessons, or "higher power" that may come. We may not be open to the invitation of learning, seeing how the incidents were meant to be, or how they will affect us or give us the knowledge to make choices in the future. We are probably not even conscious of this at the time because most of us have a hard time tapping into those subtle hints—hints we are given that will help us evaluate our purpose on this Earth. Some people may be lucky enough to figure this out early. For others, it may take more time.

Learning is ongoing and ever changing, so our purpose can also be developed, re-defined, and altered over time. I believe I fall into the "slow and steady" group. Each occurrence I experienced was a stepping stone to where I am now. Each step was like a piece of my puzzle, which I am still figuring out as I go. I believe I am on the right track, and I believe that everyone, in no matter what stage of their life they are, can find their puzzle pieces too.

From the day we are born, I believe all of the experiences we have and all of the people who surround us and love us help develop who we are. I had a pretty normal childhood: loving parents, three younger siblings, grandparents, and an extended family of aunts, uncles, and close cousins around often. I was probably pretty sheltered, and, looking back, my life was fairly easy (except for maybe during those awkward years of age twelve to fourteen, which were not easy at all!). If there were any real issues going on, I was oblivious to them.

Things changed for me the summer after my high school graduation. I believe the traumatic event that took place that summer was the beginning of a chain of experiences that would start to shape me and where life-changing hints were given, which I did not recognize at the time.

It was a day in early August, and my parents and younger siblings were on vacation out west for two weeks. I stayed home and was working at a local grocery store. One day, some of my relatives came into the store looking very distressed and told me to come with them as they had something important to tell me. Fear came over me because my first thought was that something had happened to my family on vacation. They told me something I never expected to hear. My cousin, who was just six months older than me, and who I had been very close to, had taken his own life. I was in shock and felt very sick. I think I remember blurting out "That's stupid!" or something like that. I did not understand how that could have happened or what he had done—or why. I went through that funeral without my immediate family who could not drive back in time. I stayed close to my cousin's younger sister, and we never really grieved. We didn't really know how to. This horrible incident started to manifest itself in me physically, but I did not know this at that time.

Within two weeks of my cousin's funeral, I moved to college. I was excited to go but very nervous. I found out very quickly that classes, homework, and tests were much harder in college. I did not have to make too much effort to receive A's in high school, but I was struggling in most of my classes here. The stress of the new environment plus not getting enough sleep, eating unhealthy foods, not exercising, and consuming alcohol were taking a toll on my body.

Within a few months of being there, I began experiencing excruciating abdominal pain in my upper right side. The constant pain would last about three days, and I could not eat nor sleep during the episodes, and nothing seemed to dull the pain except for alcohol, which I used moderately to get through the days and nights. The campus doctor did not know how to help me and really had no answers. If this was not enough to deal with, I started experiencing very heavy menstrual periods that would last for weeks and were hard to manage when I was supposed to be sitting in classes all day. Again, the campus doctor did not know how to help me and suggested I go home to see my family physician.

Back then, we did not have computers at school, so Googling my symptoms were out of the question. I did try to research as much as I could at the library, and so began my interest in the digestive system, hormones, and natural health solutions. I diagnosed myself with hormonal imbalance, including adrenal issues and gallbladder problems. I changed my diet, cut way down on alcohol, tried to get more sleep, and got a bit more exercise. All of this helped, but—lucky for me—I was not cured yet. My interest in natural health and finding the answers to my problems continued.

In many ways, I wish my interest in nutrition and health would have made me pursue this as a major, but there were other plans for me and things that I had to experience first.

My major ended up being psychology and criminal justice. The psychology choice, I really feel, was my fascination with emotions and understanding how the brain works. I believe that I was driven to help people in this way and that this was influenced by my cousin's suicide. This area of study led me to work with adults and children with developmental disabilities and psychiatric diagnoses. Working with this type of clientele was one of my stepping stones to learning compassion and acceptance of all types of people: people who were suffering and in need of an advocate—someone who would understand them and help them live a more fulfilling and happy life. I did this job for ten years, but I knew there was something else I was supposed to do eventually.

I was still having some health issues, and, on my own time, I was learning more about supplements and herbs through a good friend. I was attending any natural health seminar or class I could. I started "experimenting" on myself with these supplements, herbs, and natural foods, and really began feeling much better.

When I got pregnant with my first of three children, I submerged myself into natural health. I had an excellent and easy pregnancy and a very healthy baby boy. When I got pregnant with my second son, I decided it was time to make my love and passion for natural health official. As soon as son number two was born, I quit my job and began attending school for my Masters in nutrition and natural health. While still in school, I had my third child, my daughter. Two of the best decisions I ever made: staying home with my children when they were small, and going back to school to pursue a career I would absolutely love. Of course, this was all part of the intentions laid out for me.

I now own and run a natural health clinic. I have also joined together with a few other wonderful practitioners of natural health, and we have created a synergistic place of compassion, understanding, and emotional and physical healing—my dream, but also I believe part of my purpose here.

Many clients have said things over the years such as, "Thank you for believing in me and helping to save my life," or "I am so glad I finally know what is wrong with me and that there is hope for me to heal." I know that I had to go through my own pain, healing, and stepping-stones of learning to become an effective healer. I also now know this was the intention the "Higher Power" had for me, and I am glad I was open to being led down this path. It has been a most wonderful and fulfilling experience for me so far, but I know there is more to come and I am open to the invitation!

About the Author

Dee Dee Delkamp lives at her home in Wisconsin with her husband and three teenage children.

She is a licensed, certified nutritionist, board certified colon therapist, and herbal therapist. She has been trained in hair tissue mineral analysis, adrenal stress index testing, hormonal balancing, and gastrointestinal testing/stool analysis.

Dee Dee is the owner of the Optimal Health Center and co-founder/owner of HopeWell Healing Center in Madison, Wisconsin. Her clients experience healing through many holistic and natural therapies.

http://www.theoptimalhealthcenter.com/
http://www.hopewellhc.com/

Anxiety to Awesomeness: The Power to Change Anything

———— ∞∞∞ ————

Glenyce Hughes

I remember it like it was yesterday. Sitting in heavy traffic downtown Calgary, I was on my way to the usual bed and breakfast I stay at when I work in the city . . . thinking about the clients and sessions I had starting in a couple hours . . . getting a bit annoyed with the guy next to me as his music was so loud, it was making it hard to hear the Wayne Dyer audio I was listening to.

As I was looking around at traffic, I realized I could not move as there were cars all around me, and we were in a traffic jam. With that realization, something overtook me like I had never experienced before. My heart started racing; it felt like a million elephants were standing on my chest. I couldn't breathe, I started sweating, and all I could think was, "I have to get out of the car!" I knew that could end my life. I opened the window, hoping that would help. It didn't. I kept repeating to myself to calm down and that everything was going to be OK. I didn't believe it. I was pretty sure I was going to die.

Luckily, the traffic started moving, and I was able to get to a parking lot and get out of the car. My legs were like jelly, and I was in shock. What the heck was that?

This was the first of many panic attacks for years—all when I was in situations where I felt out of control. Most often when in a vehicle.

Just a few months after my experience in Calgary, I was in Shanghai, China, visiting a friend. She met me at the airport, and we took a cab the hour-long drive to her place. Within minutes, I felt out of control, which set off a panic attack. Unfortunately, this set the scene for the rest of my week in China, and all I could think of while there was when I can go home.

The panic attacks were so intense that I got to the point where I couldn't travel in a vehicle with anyone unless my husband or I was driving. My life started getting smaller and smaller. I had to say *no* to more invites than *yes*.

Looking back, this had been building for years. I wouldn't travel any great distance with people I didn't know. I always told myself it was only because I didn't know them and it would be uncomfortable socially. I wasn't willing to acknowledge what was really going on.

I used all the healing modalities I knew to change it. They only helped for a short time. I took new classes and courses looking for the solution. Once again, they also only worked for a short time. Every time I thought I found the answer, I would experience another attack.

Along with the fear of the panic attacks, I was also very ashamed of them. There were very few people I talked to about this. After all, I was running a successful healing business; if I couldn't fix myself, no one would trust that I could assist them with their problems.

I hit rock bottom in 2010. My husband and I were driving to the closest city, about a two-hour drive just for some fun and shopping. Something we had done thousands of times before. Halfway there I had an attack. There was no reason. I wasn't feeling out of control, it just happened. I spent an hour in a fast-food restaurant's washroom before we turned around and went home. I cried and cried. I decided that life beyond my house was no longer possible. None of the tools I had worked. Nothing was changing it. Basically, at thirty-eight years of age, my life was over.

The next morning, when I woke up, I knew that couldn't be it. I just knew there had to be something else. I was missing something. I had healed and dissected every part of my past that would cause this. I had had countless sessions with professionals around the world and I had done all the things my spiritual books told me to do: forgive, love, surrender. What was I missing? Was there anything that could give me life back?

In January 2011, I started listening to a new online radio show. The show shared tools from a modality I had never heard of before: Access Consciousness®. It was fascinating information, and I was intrigued. On the third show, they shared something I had never heard of before.

We are all very aware of other people's thoughts, feelings, and emotions. Some of us, like myself, are more aware than others. Way more aware. Since we have never been taught this, we assume every thought, feeling, emotion, and body sensation is ours, when it isn't. In fact 98 percent of what we are thinking and feeling isn't ours. *Wow!*

This started me thinking about the panic attacks. Is it possible they aren't mine? That was the craziest thing I had ever considered, because, let me tell you, when you are going through them, they are real—and they have to be mine. Don't they?

They suggested we start asking the question of "Who does this belong to?" to every thought, feeling, and emotion. And if it felt lighter when you asked it, it wasn't yours. You were just picking it up from people around you. Most of us are so aware, we can pick this up not only from people physically close to us, but also from those in the next house, the next town, and even the next country.

Once you asked the question, you would then ask it to "return to sender with consciousness attached", which meant you would send it back to wherever it originated with the energy for that person to change it if they chose.

It seemed too simple, yet I was willing to try anything. Later that day, I was sitting around a pool and had the thought of ordering a burger for lunch. The restaurant that served the pool made the best burgers, and it was lunch time. Then I remembered to ask the question, "Who does that belong to?"

Imagine my shock when the desire for the burger went away. *What? How could that be?* I figured it had to be just a fluke. Within twenty minutes, a guy sitting a few chairs away had his burger delivered for lunch. *Wow! I really am aware—super aware!* I broke out giggling, wondering just how many burgers had I eaten over the years for other people?

I continued to use the question for everything. My brain started feeling less full. What I would have called every day normal stress started to go away. It is difficult to put it into words, but the space it created was phenomenal. I had never experienced it before.

Along with using the question, I also started acknowledging how aware I was. When I would meet a person and judge how they had their hair styled, I knew this awareness wasn't mine. Instead, I acknowledged that I was aware that person didn't like their hair that day and that my awareness picked it up.

I took it even further. The judgments that I have about me, are they mine? Or could I also be picking those up from others? Is it possible I am not as judgmental as I have judged myself to be?

With using the question and other tools from Access Consciousness®, the panic attacks started fading away. The true test came in 2012 when I chose to go to Costa Rica to take the training to become a certified facilitator of the program. Once you arrived at the airport, it was a two-hour drive to the resort. Was this truly possible for me? Or would I end up getting back on the plane when I arrived? I was willing to take the risk.

Not only did I not have a panic attack, but I also enjoyed the ride, seeing a new country for the first time. From that moment, I knew I had my life back. I knew I could truly start living again.

I now travel the world, sharing the tools from Access Consciousness® to anyone who is willing to listen. In fact, I am writing this chapter from a remote part of Guatemala, which we had hired a driver for for the four hours to get to the dock, where a boat picked us up to get to this amazing piece of paradise. In the recent past, I couldn't have chosen this. There are not enough words to describe how grateful I am that I now can.

My target is for everyone to know that you *can* change anything. You have the ability within you to change what isn't working in your life into a life filled with ease, joy, and glory. I know this because I did.

About the Author

Glenyce Hughes is an inspirational author, speaker, professional medium, radio host, and facilitator of infinite possibilities. She empowers you to live your phenomenal life as she guides you to tap into your true potency, potential, and all the amazing infinite possibilities. A true luminary, she's inspired thousands around the world through her radio shows, writing, classes, tele-calls, groups, and individual sessions.

http://www.glenyce.net/

Real Eyes

———— ∞∞∞ ————

Greg Wilson

I am living proof that life is beautiful, ever-expanding, and worth every step of the journey!

"God, get me out of this one, and I'll never drink again!" I was once again praying to the porcelain god. A trail of vomit covered a path from my front door to the toilet. I had been out all night again on a drunken, bar-hopping, hell-raising good time.

Or so I thought!

I found myself once again hung over, sick, and depressed. If I was aware of anything, it was that my body ached and my head hurt and that I felt dead inside. The guilt and shame was almost too much to bear. I even thought about suicide again so I could just end it all and be done with myself. You see, I was not *at ease*. I was *diseased!*

I was a shy, sensitive kid while growing up in a small town in South Carolina. I had a rough time emotionally as a child and did not feel very connected to others. It seemed to me that the world was confusing and frightening. In my mind, I just couldn't do anything right. Although I was thirty years old, my perceptions, beliefs, and attitudes were like those of a fourteen-year-old's. You see, I had the body of a thirty-year-old, but emotionally I was very immature. By now, most of my childhood schoolmates were becoming successful, raising children, and doing all the other things people do as adults.

I felt left behind, abandoned, and ashamed.

As time went on, I became more aware of myself and of the choices that I had been making all my life—the choices to associate with certain people or to think a certain way. I was full of resentment, fear, and self-pity. I had a vibration that resonated with Hell, and I attracted Hell! Awareness became my first step in starting to grow up. I was becoming more conscious, and my perceptions of myself and this world started transforming. Awareness of how I had wasted my life became acute and painful. The pain and the desire to change became greater than any temporary relief that I could get from alcohol or drugs.

The journey into the darkness of alcohol and drug addiction had taken me to a very dark and lonely place. I learned some important concepts along my journey. I learned a lot about the darkness, and I learned *a lot* about the light. The darkness fed my addiction, and the light gave me life and happiness. I began to associate the darkness with resentment, fear, envy, and self-pity. I began to associate the light with gratitude, acceptance, forgiveness, and love. Therefore, perceptions, beliefs, and attitudes became keys in understanding myself and this world.

My recovery has been a journey inward and upward, learning to know and love myself as I came to know and love God. I have learned the importance of transforming ignorance into wisdom, chaos into harmony, and fear into love. In my opinion, recovery is about the transformation of one's self-awareness and one's relationship to the world.

I had hit rock bottom in 1994 at the age of thirty-one. I was sick and tired of being sick and tired. On a Sunday morning, May 15, 1994, I woke up with another severe hangover. I knew my life had to change. I started to attend support group meetings and found some hope there. I went to meetings every night of that same week. The next Friday night, I was invited to visit another hurting addict after the meeting. I volunteered to go on that visit, thinking it would be good for me. I remember thinking that this felt good because we were going to help someone in real need. We were in her home for about two hours, visiting and giving her support.

I left there and drove around town for about an hour, feeling somewhat anxious but hopeful. I finally went home to my apartment where I lived by myself and went to sleep. The next morning, I had a very profound spiritual awakening. I felt a supernatural presence in the room with me. I felt like liquid love was being poured out everywhere. For the first time in my life, I realized that there is a living

God. A bird began to chirp loudly outside my window. The bird's chirp seemed to resonate through my whole being. I looked at the window and screamed out loud, "What are you trying to tell me?" It was an experience that I can remember like it was this morning. I felt God speak to my heart and say things like, "Surrender", "Relax, and let me take over now", "Your running is over!"

I began to cry. I fell to my knees and felt reborn. It was like I was finally awakened from a deep sleep. The obsession for drugs and alcohol was gone, and I have not been the same person since that day.

I went to my parent's home and told them what had happened to me in my bedroom. I was crying and trying to apologize for crying so much. My father said, "Don't worry about your tears. We are crying tears of joy because this is what we have been praying about for many years." When he said this, it was like a burst of light illuminating my heart and soul. I began to believe in prayer for the first time in my life. I realized that prayer had a supernatural effect on my spiritual awakening. Life for me after this fateful day has been great and wonderful. I have had some bad days, but I have been with God—and my perspectives and personality have changed, and I have a whole new outlook on life. I have come to realize that I can abide in deep and lasting peace, no matter what is going on around me.

I have experienced how courage has helped me in my maturing process. I rely on courage to help me change the aspects of my personality that make me less than lovable. It takes courage to look honestly at myself and recognize the weaknesses of my character. It takes even more courage to sustain emotional poise and a willingness to continue in recovery. It takes courage to get at the roots of addiction. I can give up anytime and take the easy way out, or I can maintain courage and not let using alcohol and drugs be an option. It takes courage to think positively and act affirmatively. I must be aware constantly of any fear, resentment, or self-pity in myself.

I believe that, with daily practice, as I pursue these intentions, they become habits and a natural part of my manner and character. Alcohol and drugs cause a lot of difficulties. These difficulties, however, can sometimes seem easier than facing ourselves and making the changes necessary to be happy and free. The sober life is not always easy, but my worst days sober have been a lot better than my best days drunk or high. I remind myself as often as needed, "This too shall pass."

Acceptance became vital to my awakening from an unconscious state of self-destruction. I knew I needed to accept that I had a problem. This acceptance became my assent into the reality of the situation. I began searching for a new way of thinking that would create better results in my life than the old thought patterns of self-pity and fear. Acceptance was the antidote for my diseased thinking. Acceptance was the impetus that set me on the path of growing up . . . instead of throwing up! I discovered more light and truth.

With acceptance, my struggle was over. I became at peace with my past and present circumstances.

Gratitude, like acceptance and courage, became something that I had to develop and nurture. I had heard before that God will give us the wind, but we have to set the sail. In other words, I had to do my part and the footwork necessary for change. I started to believe that an attitude of gratitude helps set the sail for smooth sailing on the sea of joy.

Gratitude has immense transformational powers. I learned to use gratitude to guide me through the toughest of times. Gratitude helped me feel better when times were stressful and even more joyful when times were good. I discovered how gratitude breeds joy and kills off fear. I wanted gratitude to be a normal part of my character with a cheerful expectancy for all the good life has to offer. My intention now is to live life and to do whatever has to be done in a spirit of gratitude.

The bottom line for me is to keep surrendering, maintaining humility, and loving more with constant gratitude. I feel that I am reaching levels of fulfillment and freedom that I have never known before. Divine light has brought rebirth, purification, and purpose to life. I have realized that miracles happen when you change your perceptions, beliefs, and attitudes. I am freer, lighter, and more self-confident. Laughter and fun have become a way of life. I delight in my ability to be swept away by laughter. I have learned to lighten up. There really is a way to create beauty from ashes.

The monkey is off my back! I have seen the light! I finally see with my real eyes!

About the Author

Greg Wilson is an artist, writer, speaker, and life coach. He is a certified addictions counselor with a Master's Degree in education. He has a passion for Yoga and is a certified Yoga instructor. Greg is an avid reader, a follower of alternative health and healing, and a lover of the great outdoors. More importantly, he is a recovered drug addict.

http://www.gregwilson.org

A Life Worth Living; It's Never Too Late

~~~~~~

Janine Ripper

I t's like I have emerged from a heavy fog after years of wandering around, lost and confused, and at times screaming to get out, but not knowing how to or really believing that I ever would.

I've battled with depression and chronic anxiety for a large percentage of my life. I was a highly anxious, shy, and introverted kid. My earliest recollection of depression was at the age of fifteen, when all I did was cry, and all I wanted to do was for the world to stop so that I could get off for a while.

Being bombarded with images of supermodel perfection and grunge heroin chic, my attitudes toward myself quickly morphed into one of self-loathing. With red hair, pasty skin, and a swathe of freckles, I was a walking target for the bullies, and so I began to believe that I was fat, ugly, and worthless. As I retreated further into myself, I succumbed to peer pressure, and I started smoking, binge drinking, and starving myself. Eager for love, I ended up in compromising situations with the wrong type of older guy, resulting in further shame and setting fire to my path to self-destruction.

Surprising myself, I got into university, hopeful of pursuing my childhood passion for writing, but found myself unable to cope midway through my first year. I was exhausted from studying, working, and partying, and felt like I was out of my league at university.

I felt I was losing the plot mentally.

At the time, depression, and mental illness in general, were very taboo subjects with a large degree of stigma attached to them. With the "she'll be all right" attitude of most Australians, many believed that depression didn't exist or that it was simply a flaw in someone's personality—that it meant a person was emotional, sensitive, and weak. For many years, I really did believe this, thinking that I was overly emotional, sensitive, and unable to handle things like a normal person. I believed I was a flawed human being. And when I found myself struggling to get to classes, I decided that it was about time I talked to someone, so I dragged myself to see the counselor on campus, who got me to open up about my dark thoughts, childhood, and self-esteem issues. She also talked to me about depression, which was an eye-opener, and the first time I acknowledged that I had a mental illness.

I managed to graduate four years later, and took to traveling the world, as travel was the only thing at the time I was passionate about. It was also a form of escapism—but it's hard to escape your brain. On returning home, I felt confident, happy, and free, but the slippery slope was waiting for me right where I had left it.

I threw myself into work, falling into a career as a project manager. I was a success, receiving recognition and winning project management awards, but became trapped by my success, people-pleasing tendencies, loyalty, and never-say-die attitude. In hindsight, this wasn't the wisest of career choices for someone with chronic anxiety, and so I burned out more than a few times.

Throughout all of this, I met a wonderful man who made me feel beautiful and like I could do anything. He also helped me through some of the darkest periods of my life as the stress of my career and the grief from the death of my Nan took hold. He also got me to rediscover the pleasures of food. . . .

Jumping forward to 2012, with the year culminating in a trip to China where we walked the Great Wall, life was looking good. Reinvigorated and loved up, we returned home on a high. That lasted two weeks, ending in a freak accident where my partner nearly died.

The near-death experience of a loved one has a way of jolting you into reality. Finding him on the floor and not breathing, at a complete loss as to what to do, I felt helpless. He was lucky to survive, and the long road to recovery continues to this day. On the good days, I call the accident a "gift". On the bad days, I wish like hell that it had never happened.

But in reality, it was the start of an awakening for us both.

Stress has a funny way of kicking you in the ass. In 2013, after getting through the hardest part of the recovery and getting engaged, I had a car accident in the driveway of our home—my third car accident in one and a half years. I call it my personal message from the Universe, as it really didn't want me to leave the house that day. The Universe was telling me to stop.

I had developed eczema on my face and had been suffering from irritable bowel syndrome (IBS), pain, night sweats, bad circulation, dizziness, nausea, forgetfulness, and panic attacks for years. There was also an increasing sense of brain fog that just wouldn't shift. It was as if there was a cloud over my entire world from the moment I awoke until the time I went to sleep. I couldn't even work full time anymore—my whole life was impacted, and I was just so incredibly tired. . . .

I'd consulted with all types of doctors, specialists, and gurus over the years in the search for "an answer". I'd also gone on a number of "allergy" diets—or what I call "air diets"—removing wheat, gluten, dairy, sugar, wheat, alcohol, and more from my diet. I'd tried supplements, massages, and acupuncture, consulted with counselors and psychics, and had crystal healings. But nothing cured me.

And it was just getting worse.

After the car accident, I was struck by the realization that I was chronically stressed and that if I didn't do something to drastically change my life, then something a whole lot more serious was going to happen to me.

With true moments of realization comes change. There is no other option.

That realization flipped my focus from depression to anxiety. I had focused on my depression and the physical symptoms for so long, but I had neglected to pay any attention to the anxiety.

And at the age of thirty-six, the fog started to lift.

I finally tuned in and listened attentively to my heart, my body, and my mind. And as I did so, my body started telling me that there was one cause to my problems—and one cause only. It was me. I

71

had been making myself sick for the longest of times, and my poor body had been screaming at me to stop. But I had tuned out.

As soon as I made the decision to put myself first, with my health and wellbeing at the forefront, my life began to change. Good health, maintaining balance, and my overall wellbeing became the guide I used to make all of my decisions. This led to one of the hardest decisions I have ever had to make—one that I had been putting off for a very long time: I quit my job and left my successful career in project management behind me, choosing to bow out of the corporate world at the same time. With no savings, and no real idea of what to do next, this was one of the gutsiest things I had ever done, and I was absolutely terrified. But I also truly believed that it was the right thing to do.

Ever since then, my whole world changed. I feel like a shroud has been lifted off of me, and I feel *happy*. I had taken the plunge and started my own business, and I am writing like I've never written before. Being a writer: it was my dream—one that I had believed was unattainable and would never happen. But strange things happen when you throw caution to the wind and put your life in the hands of the Universe. . . .

To help myself heal, I embraced mindfulness. This has helped me break the "fight or flight" response my body was so accustomed to. It has also helped me focus on living more in the now, rather than in the past, the future, or in the stories my mind was telling me. I have also embraced Hatha Yoga, which has helped me to become more in tune with my body.

As a result of the mindfulness practice, I now accept that "I am enough", and choose to look at others and myself with non-judgmental eyes and loving kindness. This has helped me release the shame I had been carrying around for years, and I can proudly say I am no longer ashamed. I am no longer ashamed of my depression or anxiety. I am no longer ashamed of who I was and what I have done in the past. I am no longer ashamed of who I am now. In fact, I am proud of what I have come through and of surviving. It has made me the woman I am today, and I love her, warts and all.

If my journey has shown me anything it is this: it is *never* too late to change the path you are on, and that there is never a "right" time for anything . . . so what better time than now?

Life is so worth living.

About the Author

Janine Ripper is a writer, blogger, social media addict, mentor, and coach. After a lengthy career in project management, and more than a few burnouts, Janine left the corporate world to live a more healthy and balanced life and to pursue her lifelong passions for writing and travel.

Janine is an advocate for mental health, and shares her personal experiences to help others and to combat the stigma associated with mental illness.

http://www.janineripper.com

From Despair to Aware and Healing Life, Body, and Soul

———— ⌘ ————

Tracey Nichols

I was once shy with no self-esteem or confidence, and felt so inferior and insecure to the point that I'd automatically consider myself "wrong" if anyone had a different opinion to mine.

Married and with two young sons, I woke up one morning with severe lower back pain and was completely bedridden for six months. In incredible agony, I hated showering or going to the toilet. Experiencing many tests and treatments, only several chiropractic sessions made movement slightly easier, but improvement soon stopped. I was diagnosed with "degeneration of the facet joint", which should have *worsened* and put me in a wheelchair.

With only my husband's love and support, I ended up suffering depression. I found myself with no physical or emotional support from external family. Their constant rejection and with my feeling of being unloved, as well as the daily verbal abuse from a negative neighbor, took its emotional toll on me and my self worth.

I started becoming Spirit wise, and learning about mind, body, and spirit, while crawling back from the bathroom. Hearing a white witch doing a candle healing spell on television, and because doctors and treatments weren't helping, I watched the segment. I began years of reading about Wicca, the elements, crystals, magical herbs, color therapy, Spirit Guides, Angels, Archangels, Deities, the Universe, Animal Guides, Deceased, and many forms of divination, including tarot and oracle cards, which I now use professionally.

I learned about chakras, positive intentions, affirmations, energy healing, and anything that contributed to making positive changes in one's life.

I performed many self chakra balancings and several healing, happiness, and self-empowerment rituals. I read that 95 percent of physical symptoms are emotionally based, and lower back pain indicates not feeling supported. As a friend pulled away months before, and with the lack of family support, this resonated as true and helped me believe the body responds to our emotions, so I included affirmations of "support". With the positive affirmations, rituals of intent, and chakra healing, my back pain started to reduce so that I could begin helping my husband by doing easy household chores.

Though physical healing had begun, for several years I stayed housebound. Being anywhere for only half an hour, I'd end up in so much pain that I'd be bedridden again for several days, my husband would have to take me home. I happily stayed housebound because we both preferred me in less pain, smiling and laughing, than to go out and cause more suffering. My husband continued to do all the shopping, errands, and "visiting" on his own. Emotional healing was up and down, as the lack of support, love, or visits from family contributed to both my continued physical pain and depression.

I continued reading, learning, performing self-healing, doing chakra work, performing rituals, practicing self empowering affirmations, changing thought patterns and perception of thinking, and manifesting better outcomes, all which helped me continue healing, physically and emotionally.

Financially, we only had money to pay the bills. Learning that our thoughts of "only having enough money to pay the bills" was creating the exact situation we were experiencing; we used the same methods to transform our financial situation. By working on chakras, positive thinking, and a variety of wealth-attracting affirmations and rituals, and becoming aware of signs and synchronicities, we eventually found circumstances changing that improved our financial situation. We were finding ourselves no longer struggling with money and able to afford more than just paying the bills.

Confidence, happiness, and finances growing, and pain decreasing, helped me feel and become worthy of achieving more.

I was proving that thoughts manifest, and working with these methods was changing our lives.

During this time of transformation, we lost our elderly dog. I spiraled into depression again; however, this time it was worse. I'd wake up and "cry" simply because I was "still alive". With only the love of my husband, and still feeling unloved from children and family, I dealt with my pain, depression, and loss virtually on my own. The "unlove" I was constantly shown from family was always the major factor for my depression, especially at that point now that it included the loss of my faithful pet. After two years, I declared, "I don't want to be like this," and intuitively heard, "You know what to do." I knew this meant all the methods that helped before, so I made the *decision* to "change" and dedicated myself to self-healing and to my own happiness and wellbeing, and I used what I had learned and experienced to "lift myself up out of the darkness" once more.

My continued learning of self and inner healing methods, and making my emotional healing and wellness a daily priority, I gained enough healing and confidence to begin learning from teachers. With further healing and confidence, I went to learn and be attuned to Reiki from a wonderful woman who stayed in my life. Within only two weeks of giving myself Reiki twice a day, I found myself able to go out for over an hour at a time and come home smiling. This was the hugest improvement in my life and in the life of my family.

However, though seeing the benefits of Reiki, I still didn't get external family support and had little opportunity to practice on others. This is why I host Reiki shares for students to practice, as well as giving them the opportunity to receive. Learning to "receive" was another lesson I learned on my path to being healthy and happy.

I couldn't keep Reiki to myself. Although I learned it for self-healing only, and could not practice much except on my husband, children, and pets, I started my professional healing practice, and with the help from Angels and my husband, I began helping others with Reiki treatments. This not only helped teach me more about healing and becoming more spiritually aware, but it also increased my confidence and sense of self-worth.

Going forward in Reiki and becoming a Reiki Master/Teacher, I was physically and emotionally strong enough to attend larger psychic and healing workshops, most of which I use in my business, Spirit Wisdom. I started doing Angel readings and even started teaching Reiki and becoming-Spirit-wise mini-workshops. Then we had an estrangement with our eldest son. With constant situations with teachers, school social workers, and doctors, we asked whether he had ADD, I was always told, "No." As they had more students and more education, we believed them; so we didn't "change" to bring him up differently to his brother.

However, ten years later, he was diagnosed with ADD, but the emotional damage it caused him and us was done; and the more we tried helping him, the more he "hated" us. After several traumatic years, he left us for a final time and didn't return for five years. He was lost to us in every sense of the word. Only ever wanting to be a "mum", this was the most painful thing I had ever experienced, including the loss of my dog. My readings showed there'd be no change for five years, and I was always guided to focus my energies expanding my healing and reading practice.

Helping others helped me stay as strong as I could. Meditation, Reiki, working with Spirit, chakras, positive thinking, and intentions, and determined to create something different to what we were experiencing, I managed to get through another very painful time of my life. Making better choices, things changed for him also. Exactly five years later, he was back in our lives with the expectation of our granddaughter, and we saw him for the first time the day she was born. We became a family again, and he was best man at his younger brother's wedding.

Having experienced physical, emotional, and financial issues; working with chakras, intention, positive thought, Reiki, psychic and spiritual development; becoming aware of Guides and Angels, signs, and symbolism; and learning the importance of personal inner power, happiness, and wellbeing, I proved in my own life that we *can* change our lives. And by our thoughts, beliefs, and actions, along with the help of Spirit, it is possible to achieve what you thought impossible, and you can improve your life, body, and soul.

I have since successfully and harmoniously dealt with the death of my father and two elderly pets only three months apart. I then dealt with my mother's death without falling back into depths of depression, because I became stronger, emotionally and mentally.

I've learned the following that may help you too:

- *Never* give your power away to others, no matter how educated, wealthy, sophisticated, or "powerful" you *think* they are.

- Positive affirmations and the associated chakra create a better *internal* you and help create a better *external* life *for* you.

- Balancing chakras, cutting etheric cords, removing psychic daggers, and cleansing and shielding auras help keep you clear and protected from negative energies, negativity, and influences of others and of your environment.

- "Listen" to your body and what it's "saying".

- The effort and intention you put into yourself, your happiness, and your wellbeing are worth it, not just for yourself, but for all those around you.

- *Never* give up. You, your happiness, and your dreams and goals are worth fighting for.

- A positive attitude, finding the lessons in all situations, expecting positive outcomes, and working with Spirit and the Universe can change and improve your life, and you could achieve what you thought impossible. As with the Law of Attraction, like attracts like.

- Becoming Spirit wise, more aware, and working for the good of all bring blessings that you will experience daily.

Becoming Spirit wise and following Spirit's guidance for healing life, body, and soul—and generally seeing everything in life from a higher perspective—have helped me cope with life's challenges. Reiki, Angelic therapy, chakras, self-talk and mind-set transformations, and choosing to become more "aware" have positively changed me *and* my life. I am happy and feel blessed. I believe with dedication to happiness and wellbeing, it can be the same for anyone.

About the Author

Tracey, owner/founder of Spirit Wisdom, teaches Reiki and Becoming-Spirit-Wise workshops. She has created SYMBOLIC SIGNS & SYMBOLS Wisdom Cards, is a qualified Reiki Master/Teacher; Angel intuitive; and chakra/aura, crystal, and dream therapist. She is also qualified in Feng Shui, Indian head massage, and paranormal investigations. Tracey teaches through psychometry, tarot and wisdom card readings, meditation, monthly groups, Reiki, and chakra/aura and crystal therapy treatments in East Maitland, NSW, and in local festivals, expos, and correspondence across the world.

http://www.spiritwisdom.com.au

The Beyondness of Things

Nathan Dennett

I measure my own success by my heart, and I also freely admit that I live by it. I judge my own success on my own terms. I live my personal success by how I sleep at night. Yet, where I am right now isn't where I was meant to be. I am living the life that was never even in my mind's eye ten years ago.

I always felt that teaching and education were why I was put on Earth. I graduated with a Bachelor of Education, hoping for that full-time position where I could take hold with vigor and have the rest of my life educating in schools. I felt that I was in my element, that I was set for life doing the job I always wanted to do.

It was not one but two car accidents, ten minutes apart and the same woman who hit me twice! It threw my world into pain, suffering, and anguish—a negative black fog. My first accident was minor. It was an accident, no harm. The second one destroyed my car—the most valuable thing I owned—and dumped my immediate teaching career (I lost my current teaching terms as I became ineffectual). I also nearly failed my university degree, as I could hardly sit through tutorials and concentrate.

I am a clean living person. I do not drink alcohol, smoke, or take medication. (I don't even drink tea or coffee!) Yet, the "helpful" pain medication would wipe me out for hours and days. . . . It was an awful state to be in. I was ensconced by the black fog of despair, which had descended and wrapped itself around my brain, my body, and my life.

I had never felt like this before. My brain was fuzzy, my body got heavy, my functioning started to slow down dramatically, and my heart dimmed. I struggled through university with help from my friends. I became depressed and gained weight. Eventually, I forced myself to minimize the painkillers, go to physiotherapy, and work through the pain of my totally screwed-up spine. To make matters worse, six months later, I was in another car accident as a passenger.
. . .

This was shaping up to be a Charlie Brown year. I remember Charlie Brown cartoon characters getting excited for Halloween, dressing up, and having all the fun going from house to house to scare people and collect candies. Yet, when Charlie gets home, he finds that people keep putting rocks in his bag. *Good grief!* And to say the least, my own dreams and intentions were weighed down with rocks. It was a dark time. I couldn't get past the why's, the why not's, the woe is me, or the shoulda woulda coulda mentality. Mea maxima culpa (through my most grievous fault).

What changed everything was finding hot Yoga. The teacher was a lovely American woman who welcomed me into the small class with "Look beyond what you can do or cannot do, because either way you are right! Jump in with your eyes open!"

The teacher was right. When you jump in with your eyes open, you see a whole new world waiting that you would have missed if you had kept them shut or focused on one point. I felt different with this Yoga teacher—I felt weightless, the fog was dispersing, the pain was bearable. And even though I could not do everything, I went back every day for a month. I felt like I had achieved something positive for myself. My heart started shining through the fog.

My car accidents revealed to me that negativity is heavier on the heart than positivity. Positivity is light, buoyant, and how life *should* be. We can exude lightness. We can be bursting with radiance. When our electrical charge is positive, we have mind-blowing experiences. We can rebound when positively charged. To keep negativity at bay, I believed I needed a lot of positive experiences to keep the evenness, the equality, the balance within my being.

My life paradigm began to shift at once with my Yoga. It was the little achievements within the class that really helped me get off painkillers, start teaching again, drive a new car, and get my weight down again. The Yoga was positively charging my spine, my brain, and every single cell of my body. My blood was pumping, my muscles stimulating—my healing created itself.

It was way beyond therapy. It was like being reborn.

Then a crazy event appeared on the studio calendar: the Australian Yoga Asana Championships. Never heard of it before, didn't know there existed such a thing, but my studio owner said I should go in for fun and show my family and friends how I had transformed my broken, battered self into this happier, healthier young man.

The basic championship guidelines: three minutes, seven poses, alone on a stage in front of a lot of people, being scored on balance, flexibility, strength, and a host of other boxes to tick or cross. I accepted the challenge! I worked through my routine daily. I found a focus for my health and wellbeing—it was all within Yoga.

Competition date arrived—I was trembling with excitement and trepidation. This would be the place I get to prove how I lifted the fog, found balance, and regained my composure. It was like my own private science research being proven to the world at long last!

The crowd was eager to see this Asana championship. They were thrilled with each competitor by means of their thunderous applause. The intimidating Indian national judges were tough scorers, but honest in admiration.

As I stood before the crowd and judges, I executed my compulsory poses well. My optional postures were Urdhva Dhanurasana (Wheel Pose), and these showed my impressive new back-bending skill. Also, Vrischikasana (Scorpion Pose) from a supported headstand to show my regained arm and shoulder strength. These poses were the pinnacle for me. Even now, I still love to practice them before every Yoga class.

I finished within the allocated time, I executed every posture. I was graceful, flexible, and strong. Unfortunately, a fall out of a pose is a major deduction, therefore I didn't get a medal, but I did come in fourth place—I was over the moon! From a crash test dummy to a fearless Yoga competitor within eighteen months . . . I would *never* have guessed!

Post-performance, I was backstage with the biggest grin on my face and my hands shaking. I wanted to do it all again! This was my paradigm shift and a pivotal point in my life. This was the loss of my fears—the culmination of effort, body, brain, and heart.

The championships have left a great impression on how I held myself throughout and how I regained composure when I wrongfully fell forward in Scorpion to land my feet on the floor in front of my hands instead of on my head. I kept my forearms on the floor, walked my feet back around, and skipped back up into the pose. If you fall off the Scorpion, jump back on again!

I did do it again. It would be another three years before I won the National Titles. Each year I competed, I won medals, and I also represented Australia three times at the International Yoga Asana Championships.

Talk to any person who does marathons, or cycles up a mountain, or swims an ocean, and they'll tell you they *train their bodies for competitions* with total commitment, big sacrifices, and no guarantees of winning. *I competed to train my body* back to health with minimal sacrifices and my guarantee was getting myself back to a state of balance. Everybody has the right to lose the fear and do something for themselves! My medals were not the success I was looking for; they were what I gained for looking after myself.

Now I judge regional and national championships in a variety of countries and in the International Yoga Asana Championships each year. I get to travel the globe to teach, talk, and practice Yoga.

So the Western view of Yoga is an exercise held in a walled space for an hour; you move your body around and chant. The Eastern view of Yoga is that of a lifestyle, a combination of aspects that are pulled together by the self—the way you act, think, eat, move, clean, work, behave. . . . *That* is Yoga! *You don't even know you are doing Yoga—even if you have never done Yoga, you are doing Yoga!* Looking back, it was exactly about showing what I had struggled with and pushed through to simply get back to easing through life again. It was never about gaining medals; it was about regaining life. It was about finding my heart and moving out of the dark.

Here and now, I am surrounded by people who share my love and make life easy. I have three jobs that I love, that give me freedom to move, work, and play, like no other job could do. I educate in schools, I promote health with Yoga, I marry happy families. I even found my wife in my Yoga class! None of this could have happened if I had not lost my fears each step of the way, measured my own success, and pushed on through.

I found that fear can be a negative emotion, but I now believe, at times, negative events are placed before you, somewhat, as a test of your *true nature*. It just takes a little courage to retrieve a sightline of action and reassemble the pieces to find a new way and a better life. I looked into the beyondness of things, accepted fate, and found my heart again.

About the Author

Nathan Dennett is a primary school teacher providing education to 5-12-year-old children; a Yoga teacher generating connections for people to create personal growth and wellbeing; a Yoga Studio owner offering a community hub of health, happiness, and healing; and a civil marriage celebrant for weddings and funerals—but not at the same time, please!

Nathan found life through laughter, self-growth through education, and love through the beyondess of things.

http://www.myyogasuccess.com
http://www.yogafrogs.com.au

From Darkness to Light: A Tale of Evolution

Amanda Elizabeth

My life started off with all of the necessities to be full of wellness. I came from a loving family with an exceptional mother, who raised me with an abundance of unconditional love and support. My childhood is filled with fond memories of happy times, laughter with my extended family, and loving encouragement to pursue my dreams. My upbringing set me up with all I could need to succeed, with the bonus of some wonderful role models to look up to. During my childhood, I was interested in animal rights, competitive swimming, travel, and cultures. My favorite possession was my *Children's Atlas of the World* where I would plan all my adventures far and wide. My biggest dream was to volunteer in an orphanage in Africa. I was a good kid with big dreams and an innocent heart. But even this early ambition couldn't stop the downpour of sorrow that I was about to be entrenched in.

Soon after I hit middle school, everything changed for me, and I went down an unexpected path. By age thirteen, I began to trade my achievements in athletics and in being on the honor roll for alcohol and drugs. At the new school, I was introduced to a new, older and dangerous crowd. Associating myself with this group of people exposed me to an environment where violence and abuse against women was encouraged and celebrated. At the time, I was still naïve enough to think nothing bad would happen to me. I trusted these people even when I was warned to stay away from them.

I didn't listen, and this choice would forever change my life.

One morning when I gained consciousness after a night of partying with my so called friends, I awoke horrified to the fact that I had been raped and robbed. My virginity was taken from me. After this event, I started to spiral into a confused and darker state as I was told I did something wrong—that I was to blame—and to laugh it off. I was terrified.

I became the subject of public torment when false rumors and lies spread like a wildfire. The bullying got so bad that I was secretly contemplating suicide on a daily basis. I would study how to do it and write suicide letters after a long day of harassment at school. I lived in a constant state of fear and insecurity, and felt disbelief and confusion at the fact that this horrific event could be humorous to so many young people, including my own friends. I was too scared to have a voice, so I laughed it off as my world was ripped apart.

This was my life, my nightmare by fourteen. I stopped caring whether I lived or died, and my actions showed this. I never told people at school or my family what really happened or how bad things were for me. Luckily, my mother sensed something was wrong and put me into a different school. This was an action I credit with saving my life, even though my descent into drugs and alcohol would progress for the next nine years.

The new school was completely different; everyone got along and treated each other well. I was blown away and met some of my soon-to-be life-long best friends here. At the time, nobody knew the reason I came or the torment I faced when out in the world; but here I got the chance to be a teenager again without the constant fear and anguish I felt every day the year before. I slowly stopped thinking that suicide was an option and embraced walking into school without being the target of hate and humiliation. It was a huge relief to feel safe and normal again.

Although things were getting better, and I was trying to distance myself from the not-so distant past, I still had a long journey filled with bad decisions and substance abuse ahead of me. A few years later, I entered into my first serious relationship. Unfortunately, we soared to new heights together in our drug use; our relationship quickly crumbled; and years of abuse, poverty, and pain took over the carefree young love we shared in the beginning. At twenty-four years old, after years of hitting rock bottom and losing the trust of my family, this toxic relationship ended for good—and my healing journey really started to take off.

During the dark years, I never held onto a job for long, I had worked at thirty different jobs by the time I was twenty-five—sometimes because of substance abuse, and sometimes because I craved doing work I was passionate about. Even though my self-esteem and confidence were shot after years of being told I wasn't good enough, I knew I was living as a dimmed version of myself, and my desire to help others never faded. It wasn't until I stumbled upon a position to work with people with disabilities that I realized my true gifts.

I was good at looking after people, and I was starting to see my potential in the helping professions. I had a close relationship with someone with schizophrenia, and I knew that my real drive was to help people with mental illnesses live their best life. I entered into the world of working in mental health and addictions, realizing that this was my true calling, my passion, and my purpose. I believe realizing a profession I was passionate about was the first step in my healing journey. There is no better gift you can give yourself.

I started to accept how much I had been through, how many people I felt had betrayed me, and how many people and situations were still causing me pain. I also felt a deep sense of grief and embarrassment within myself for how I had treated my loved ones and for how I actively damaged my mind, body, and soul. It was a hard pill to swallow, but I knew I wanted to shed the resentment, guilt, and shame. I accepted the fact that I needed to create space for healing and to work through the past if I wanted to have a bright future.

I began to be gentle with myself. Now that I was on my own, I started to take note of who I wanted to be, acknowledging and working through my destructive habits. Toxic relationships ended and positive relationships started to form. I was starting to experience the clarity of stillness and letting go. The self-love I had lost so many years ago was finally beginning to shine its light.

Practicing Yoga and meditation is where I continue to experience many breakthroughs and realizations. It was where I had discovered the roles I played in all the tough times of the past. I had a lot of forgiving and accepting to do. Forgiveness of self, of spirit, and of others. Accepting of what is and the benefit it brought to my life. The deeper I went into solitude, the deeper my understandings became. With every practice, I continue to feel lighter, and life seems to move more gracefully away from negativity and fear.

To begin my fresh start, I dove head first into all things I am passionate about: my career, travel, and wellness (being the most influential of them). I started to write poetry about my past heartache and with every line a crack in my broken heart was refilled with love. I reconnected with nature sober and joyful, accepting life's miracles as they came with open arms. I experimented with different forms of therapy and found what set me free.

By claiming responsibility and dependability back into my nature, the world travels I had always dreamed of became a beautiful reality. Volunteering abroad allowed the seas of the world to cleanse my skin in an envelope of calm and renewing energy while hiking in the Himalayas soothed my soul and enlightened my inner adventurist. The connections I've made and the energy I experienced rocked my world and continue to fuel my life with wanderlust.

Dedication and hard work manifested my life into happiness on a level I had forgotten existed. Never giving up made my dreams come true when I thought there was no hope. I realized reaching out for support when I need it and being able to be there for my family, friends, and clients are some of life's greatest gifts.

These radical experiences and realizations are the foundation of my new self. A self I love, a self I can heal, a self that has lived, and a self that has learned. A self that is grateful not only for all the good, but also for all the bad that preceded today.

My journey into evolution has been a long windy road, backtracking over mountains of insecurity and self-doubt with courage and ability pushing me on. I learned to surrender when bumps show up along the way and to use my inner wisdom and power for moving forward. I will always have flaws, and I will continue to make mistakes, but it sure feels good to be consciously awake.

Love yourself. Allow space to heal. Namaste.

About the Author

Amanda Elizabeth has been working in the field of mental health and addictions for eight years and is the founder of Healing & Harmony Inspired Wellness. Here, she provides life coaching, body work, and retreats. Amanda's passions include travel, Yoga, meditation, and assisting people to live their best life. Currently, Amanda is breaking away from the norm to live a nomadic lifestyle, learning, loving, and teaching along the way.

http://www.healingandharmony.ca

Spirited Journey

—⸎—

Chelle Fisher

The temperature had just hit 40 degrees Celsius when we started our walk into the gorge. I had discovered the night before from some local Aboriginal men that this was the gorge where their women had gone to give birth in the times before tourism. I was excited to visit this site as I was experiencing a very strong spiritual connection to this area of the Kimberley, in Australia.

The walk was quite demanding, and as we wandered deeper into the gorge, I marveled at the resilience of the women that had passed this way before me on their way to birth their young. The walls of the gorge became higher and narrower the deeper we ventured, and there were many boulders to go around or climb over. Hard enough when you are semi-fit, let alone nine months pregnant!

Upon reaching the end of the gorge, my heart leapt. It was a place of quiet beauty and serenity, totally feminine. Small palms stood as a stark contrast to the deep, ochre red of the sheer walls, and the cool air of the shaded chasm provided welcome relief. As I stood and gazed over the magnificence of the surroundings, I had a deeply moving experience. All the hair on the back of my neck stood up, and I had a shiver from head to toe. A "voice" spoke to me at that moment and told me that I was put here to use my healing. It was so stirring, tears welled in my eyes—tears of absolute joy, a feeling of deep peace enveloping me. It was as though I had just realized that this was what I was here for—I was here to help others heal, not only physically, but also spiritually and emotionally. At that moment, it all made sense—my questioning was answered.

What I had experienced stayed with me as we made our way slowly back out of the gorge, not speaking much, quietly taking in the surroundings and absorbing what had just occurred. I felt incredibly uplifted—I can still recall that feeling to this day.

I had always had the feeling that I was here for a purpose, a higher calling of some sort; however, I was never quite sure what. When I lost my brother to aggressive cancer in 1990, I was prompted to search for answers. I deepened my knowledge of the metaphysical world, the topic of reincarnation, and the whole life and the Universe bit. I read everything I could get my hands on, trying to understand why I had been robbed of his presence on this plane. His leaving also sparked a song-writing phase with me, which helped me heal through my music. Many nights were spent draped over a guitar with pen in hand, trying to make sense of it all. This devastating event in my life began my spiritual quest to understand more of the "invisible" world that surrounds us.

It was a long road. I was a young mother, only twenty-six, with three small children. I spent years with this thirst for knowledge quietly simmering in the background, never leaving, just waiting for the right time to surface. I tinkered with learning bits and pieces about different things, herbs, crystals and the like, yet nothing really gelled with me.

In 2006, my father died. This was a turning point for me. My children had all left home, I was in a job that did not fill me with excitement or fulfilment, and I had very itchy feet. My father was a wanderer, in the sense that much of his life was spent traveling the roads as a truckie, and I had certainly inherited some of this gypsy blood. During a trip to Kakadu in the north of Australia, shortly after my father's passing, my husband and I decided that we would throw our corporate hats to the wind and take to the road. So, upon our return home, we packed our belongings into our car and hit the road. This was an unbelievably therapeutic move, but it was also one that scared the hell out of us at times. Turns out, we are still traveling and loving the freedom that this brings to our lives.

Many places that we visited around the country were incredibly ancient and very spiritual, having strong connection to the Aboriginal inhabitants that had wandered the land before us.

However, as wonderful as this life was, I still felt that something was missing with me.

I began to feel a deeper spiritual stirring within me the more I discovered of my country. Many hours were spent in wonder at the sheer beauty that surrounded me. I began to make meditation part of my daily life; and, through this, I connected to things of which I had only dreamt. I started to have visions of my spirit guides, one in particular that I named Hawk. Around this time, the Universe began sending me signs that I was on the right track. I remember one morning in particular, on my daily bike ride, where a hawk flew in front of me for about a kilometer, only ten feet or so above the ground. I found myself smiling unselfconsciously during this experience. I had asked for a sign and there it was—simply by allowing myself to believe, I was being shown a confirmation that was unmistakable. I also began to dabble with reading oracle cards at this time, mainly to answer questions for myself as I was certainly not ready to put this up as part of my public face.

It wasn't until 2012 that I made the decision to do something for me. The passing of my eighty-nine-year-old mother was the catalyst for this. She was a woman who had devoted most of her life to bearing and raising eight children, often sacrificing her own wants for those of the family. Although she had achieved so much in her life, I know she held many disappointments within from not following her path, and there was much sadness in me, for her, because of this.

I didn't want to be left feeling the same lack of fulfillment in my later years, so I made the choice to act. I decided I had spent too much of my life worrying about others before myself. This was *my* time. I was ready. I believe that it was the right time—I had had to wait to spend those years ridding myself of baggage and beliefs that had kept me trapped in the same old "I'm not worthy" frame of mind. It took a lot of work, but it was amazingly liberating. It was also a bit scary, as I wasn't sure that I would be any good at what I was attempting. I knew, however, that I had to try.

So, I put it out there to the Universe. Reiki was to be my modality of choice—something about this method of healing hands called to me. As I search the internet for a teacher, one woman's name kept appearing. It was clear to me that she was to be the one to guide me. We conversed, and it felt so right that I made the appointment to study Reiki with her. One of the best decisions I have ever made.

It was with anticipation and a little trepidation that I traveled to Melbourne and did my Reiki. My goodness, the feeling I received from the learning and empowerment was incredible. The only way I can describe it was that I felt this was what I was put here for—I had come home. It was an intensely emotional experience for me also. I laughed, cried, and felt such peace that I knew it was right. It was the direction I was to follow.

I have since become a Reiki Master, and each time I have a healing session with someone it is a powerfully fulfilling experience for us both. The feeling of totally tuning in with the Universal energy and Mother Earth is indescribable.

It has taken time and effort to reach the place I am in now. However, I would not change the path I have trod. Each event, significant or trivial, has led me to where I am today, and each needed to occur to allow me to grow and accept what the Universe had in store for me. The discovery and acceptance of these gifts have been absolute blessings in my life. To deny them would be to deny my true self.

To find your path, make the decision to follow it and then embark on your journey, which can only bring peace, love, and joy to your life. It did to mine, and each time I receive a hug of thanks from a person I have helped, these feelings are magnified, and for this I am grateful.

About the Author

Chelle Fisher is a Reiki Master, mother, grandmother, and gypsy. She spends her time traveling, working, and learning around Australia on a quest to enrich the world we live in. A healer, songstress, and part-time writer, her dream is to open a wellness center and café, where all may experience health, happiness, and the joy of fresh, wholesome food.

http://www.lunamargahealing.com.au

Finding Meaning
Through Near-Death

———— ᨒᨑᨒ ————

Cynthia-Boeckmann

I was born into this world pure, innocent, beautiful, loving, and whole. Our formation, in part, is the culmination of our personal experiences with our family, community, world, personal genetics, and accumulated knowledge.

It was a hot Midwest summer, and I was seventeen going on forever. The general feeling was that summer was one of freedom, which came from trusting the world you live in and one's own invincibility. The days, I filled with softball, Frisbee in the park, and work. The nights were filled with concerts, parties, baseball, and work. I was enjoying the summer and appreciating the feelings of independence. There was only one hiccup: I didn't feel well, and I hadn't felt well for quite some time. Being raised in a home where we didn't often share our feelings, fears, or even illnesses, I kept up the appearance that everything was great.

My gang picked me up, and we were heading to the big game at the baseball field. As we pulled up and I started to exit the car, something just didn't feel right.

Suddenly, the sky went dark, and I went down.

We never made it to the game.

Immediately, I lay down, gasping for air and wondering if I was going to stay conscious. Extreme nausea and abdominal pain filled the void, and back pain made it impossible to find any position of comfort. When I began expelling black fluids and seeing only darkness before my eyes, I knew I was in trouble. What was to come, I never experienced before or since. The experience evoked feelings that would take decades to uncover. There would be no one for me to talk to. This was a totally new experience. Yet, the journey that began forever changed me.

Seven days into my hospital stay, my parents were faced with a decision. "Your daughter will be dead by the morning, or she has a 50/50 shot of survival with surgery." As I was rolled into surgery, I remember saying as the doors closed behind me, "Don't worry. Everything will be OK." Some very nice nurses were by my side as I lay on the table in a very chilly room. The small stuffed animal was in one of the nurse's pocket, looking over me. The X-rays of my lungs hung on the wall.

10 ... 9 ... 8 ... 7 ... 6 ...

Everything went black.

. . .

The following is an account of what I remember. . . .

A dim light glowed at the end of a very dark corridor. I was slowly moving—not walking or flying, but floating down so to speak. Indescribable warmth was emanating and filling the space around me. It was filling more than space—it was filling an endless emotional void deep within me. The overwhelming feeling of love, of welcome, and of being treasured completed me. I was finally going home. I was free from judgment, there were no boundaries, and I was loved unconditionally. It has forever remained a remarkable feeling and is something I never felt before or since.

Suddenly, everything went dark again. Fear overwhelmed me as I was pulled back. Out of the darkness, strange noises and arms emanated and attempted to pull me deep into a hole. As my fear grew, the shouting began: "I am alive, don't bury me; don't let them have me!" All things stopped suddenly.

I was awake, tubes in my mouth, and I was trying to speak. I needed to share the experience. The urgency of the moment took over with doctors, nurses, and family all around. I was back, but was I home? Many years later, I would learn that others had gone through similar events, and it had a name: a near-death experience.

The debate regarding the legitimacy of near-death experiences may continue; however, I am here to share what I learned through this experience, to serve others, and to support their own journeys.

The concept of death and near-death experiences was new to me. At seventeen, no one spoke about such things. The feelings I felt of being different, alone, abandoned, and unworthy continued to grow. I didn't know how to share what I experienced with those who loved me. The effect of those feelings on my formation from a teenager to independent young adult, lover, wife, and eventually a mother unsettled me occasionally and drove me at other times. The feelings of unworthiness and abandonment came from a source I did not recognize. As I continued through life I began to realize from our experiences we become empowered or victims—real or imagined—helpless or blaming.

The journey of my life is to sort out that event and understand who it created. The journey is circular, moving from empowered to victim and back again. Learning to thrive, not survive, needs tools, and my belt was empty. The gift of a second chance was presented, yet I didn't feel as though it was a gift. The void was deep, and I filled it with people and things not necessarily good for me. Eventually, the people who would become my teachers appeared.

This life-changing event brought forth all of the insecurities that previously existed, and magnified them ten-fold. The feelings of abandonment and unworthiness continued. The need to please others took over, the lack of belief in myself manifested in many ways. The emptiness I felt, and the pain it created, prompted feelings of being in it alone. Healing the pain, learning to accept the event, and the voyage to healing were just beginning two decades later. I worked, studied, tried to play, and did it all again, yet never for myself.

I now know this event was a *life-giving opportunity*.

Living life on purpose is an ongoing assignment just as growing in faith and knowing the existence of one Universal Intelligence: God, Yahweh, Creator, Elhohim, or Jehovah, the list goes on, and Source doesn't mind what we call it. Learning to thrive and to release the feelings of abandonment and unworthiness has taken time just as finding my inner courage and voice has.

As we move forward, please remember I am only a woman who experienced life-changing events. I bring forth the lessons I have learned and tools I have used to move forward. Mind-body-spirit moves as one; nonetheless, I will present a process or an idea, which personally supported my journey for each of the three areas.

MIND

George Orwell once wrote something about how childhood necessarily creates a map of reality. It is the only map we know; and no matter how old we are, at the first sign of trouble we retreat into this map.

Step One – Rewrite Your Map of Realty

Our personal belief system and vision of ourselves influence our choices and decisions, and therefore, shape the life we create. If you want to change, study, read, and discover new ideas and perspectives. Build your self-esteem, identify areas of co-dependency in your life, and allow yourself the opportunity to create independence. Stop negative self-talk and watch your dialog as you place your affairs in order. Also, know that it's okay to grieve! It helps you let go and move on in your life.

To continue moving your life forward, embrace your spirit and feel loved! Get to know yourself and your personality type. Explore the possibility of visualizing your future and using affirmations to create a life you've always dreamed of.

BODY

Thomas Jefferson firmly believed in the concept of physical exercise in creating and maintaining bodily and mental health as well. His philosophy was that a strong body makes the mind strong.

Step 2 – Redefine What Physical Health Means to You

Remember, *we are not our body*. The body is the vessel that holds the true you: the spirit, the soul, the voice. Strength in physical body creates a strong vessel for the *I AM!*

The body is merely an energetic system filled with sub-systems: nervous, cardiovascular, endocrine, respiratory, digestive, excretory, and skeletal systems working together to support, protect, and maintain a state of homeostasis.

To continue moving life forward, embrace your body by redefining the role physical health plays into your everyday life. Begin to exercise. Study and learn the importance of stress reduction. Learn to appreciate *your* body and recognize its signals. Allow yourself to cleanse, balance, and build your body.

SPIRIT

John Maxwell wrote how some people fail forward while others fail and quickly spiral downward. He continued with the thought that the difference is on the inside: the spirit of the individual.

Step 3 – Identify What Spirit Means to You

Personally, I believe in one Infinite Power and Source, which has many names. Some believe God to be in form, while others believe God to be energy and transcendent.

To continue moving forward in life, utilize prayer and meditation. Live in service to others and ask for forgiveness.

Learn to ask and surrender to what is, live in gratitude, and ask for what you need. By doing so, you will gift yourself the opportunity to begin discovering your life purpose.

The Journey

Life has been filled with joy and blessings, terror and sadness, mistakes and loss of faith. The journey I have traveled has traversed great distances, internally, externally, geographically, and physically. The silent struggle to release feelings of unworthiness and abandonment and to find my life purpose could have been sooner. However, I remain on the physical plane for a reason, and identifying my purpose led me here to you. Exploring what this means and embracing the road ahead is a gift I continue to delight in. The steps above have provided a roadmap to knowing all things are possible through God and action. I am here to serve, support, educate, and share that the power is in the moment and in remaining present.

Action is the final step.

Regardless of the level of commitment, without action, nothing is possible. Often I have asked, "How do I begin?" The answer received has been the same: *just start*. Start where you are at, and take one step each day in faith, knowing that as you so believe, the Universe will so deliver. Pinpoint the desired outcome for your life and beyond—and it will be so. Action moves energy, and energy creates. What action is waiting for you?

About the Author

Cynthia Boeckmann is a freelance writer, consultant, coach, and entrepreneur. She lives on the Big Island in Hawaii. Cynthia is a highly dynamic professional who coaches and educates on nutrition, overall health, performance, and lifestyle. Additionally, she consults with companies on personnel development, team building, and service related opportunities. Cynthia has studied the 7 habits of highly effective individuals, transcendental meditation, science of mind, and is a graduate of PSI. She enjoys creating unique health conscious snacks for friends and family, storytelling, camping, and time with her two children. She hones her writing skills on her blog and website, and shares lifestyle, nutrition, and inspirational tips on Facebook.

http://www.two-realms.com

They Get to the Beach When They Get to the Beach!

∞∞∞

Tracey Ha'aoLakainãpali

I have a vivid memory of a photo taken of me as a baby laying in my cot, laughing, gurgling, and . . . well, glowing. I remember my mother and grandmother reminiscing on many occasions about what a happy baby I was. That I rarely cried. Just smiled and happily gurgled. They indeed wondered that something might be "wrong" with me because, apparently, not crying was unusual for babies. On reflection now, from the adult who has journeyed long and far, I now know this to be the beginning of what was simply a life "path of wellness" for me.

Hawaiians teach that each of us is born as a pure bowl of light. That as we grow, stones are placed in our bowl and gradually dim our light, if we allow them. It's all about our choices. We can choose to keep the metaphoric stones in there, or we can toss them out. *Choices.* We can allow all the old hurts, memories, self-diminishing thoughts, and events that the stones represent to fill our bowl, or we can choose to take the positive learnings and let go of those stones.

Wellness for me has always been a life choice of health—physically, mentally, emotionally, spiritually. It's not a destination. Wellness is a way of being, of living daily. Now, that's not to say that during this journey of wellness I haven't experienced blips on the radar. I most certainly have! It comes with being a human! However, when one of these blips occurs, such as the melanoma I manifested many years ago, I never let it become more than that. No meteorites

100

wanted here. My immediate reaction is "What was I thinking?!" Literally, what was I thinking that created this? Being accountable for my thoughts and my actions. I know that my thoughts and words form my world, my reality 24/7. If I'm not enjoying the world or the reality I've created, it's up to me to change it.

After the melanoma was surgically removed on the same day it was diagnosed, Annie Lennox singing *Thorn in my Side* kept playing in my head. Then I realized why. Oh, those "light bulb" moments! That's how I had been referring, some years prior, to a former partner—as "just a thorn in my side". Ouch! What a clear manifestation of that thought—the melanoma representing "the thorn"! Ooh, time to toss that stone out of the bowl!

My journey of this lifetime has enjoyed the experiences of the rich diversity of many spiritual practices. The Hawaiian cultural and spiritual ways of living are what I strive to embody. *Aloha and pono.* Hawaiian words have deep complexity so simply put—love, compassion, ethics, and integrity. Their often used analogy of our journey to paddling a canoe is a reference filled with so much depth and wonderful imagery. We are all in charge of our own canoe. We are each responsible for whether or not we paddle and the direction we take. Do we paddle blindly or look for the signs? When the paddling gets a little rough or when we find we have been paddling in circles, do we give up, throw the paddle overboard, jump out, and hope that someone will jump in after us and save us?

As a practitioner and teacher for over twenty-five years, and as someone who sees the spirit greatness and potential in every person, I had become a master of jumping in after people and endeavoring to stop them from drowning. Anyone would think I was trying out for the spiritual remake of Baywatch! Then last year another of those many light bulb moments came. My physical body was experiencing painful inflammation, and I was exhausted. Not a familiar feeling for me. I'm used to being the "Energizer Bunny", whose battery just keeps on going. Due to overextending myself and my time, I had allowed myself to become depleted on many levels and had allowed some joyfulness and magic moments to dim a little. My being had some rust setting in. I had forgotten to be that gurgling, joyful baby. I had allowed others to deposit their stones in my bowl.

Time for me to sit still for a moment in my canoe, look at the stars, correct the course, and change direction. *Ho'opono pono ke ala*—make right, more right the path. Everything is *I ka pono mea*—in perfection, right place, right time, right being. That's why I've never really understood the question "Are you a person who is a glass half empty or half full?" I believe it's always full. It just keeps expanding to accommodate more joy, opportunities, and desired experiences. We simply have to remember to be in the joyfulness and aloha of every moment. The time had come for me to get a shiny, new, really big glass.

I embraced the learning and understanding that some people who come into my life, whether as family, friends, clients, students, or acquaintances, actually choose to stay in the M.E. of "Many Excuses"—rather than the M.E. of "Magical Events and Experiences". All I can show them is where to look, point out the stars to aim for; however, I have to let them paddle at their own pace. I can't tell them what to find or how to find it. All I can be is a living, shining example of what I know. To the knowledge and wisdom of my path, my journey. Valuing (yep, that's been a big one) my time, knowledge, wisdom, and journey. To speak and shine my truth.

It's not my responsibility, nor is it my right, to try and drag anyone into a canoe that they don't want to be in. Regardless of how powerful, profound, extraordinary, and magical that canoe might be. Regardless of the potential and greatness I see in them, they have to find it themselves, in their own way. I discovered there actually is such a thing as giving out too much *Aloha* to others, when they actually didn't want to receive it or didn't see themselves worthy of receiving it.

In doing that, I also recognized it was time to allow them the choices of their journey, regardless of the stormy seas I could foresee for them. Once I honored their choices and stepped away from their canoes, which were sinking with the weight of their stones, the inflammation left my body and the energy returned. It was time to refuel myself with the *Alohas*.

A client shared with me a few months ago a quote she had come across by Anne Lamott: "Lighthouses don't go running all over an island looking for boats to save; they just stand there shining." The cartoon visual of me as the lighthouse running all over the island certainly gave me another amusing light bulb moment (no pun intended). I had been that lighthouse, running wide-eyed, arms waving, trying to help them avoid the rocks and light their way to the beach. Yet, still they crashed on those rocks—or, sometimes, even paddled back out and aimed fully for them!

At the same time, as I had that insight, there were two days when a little pet rabbit that had escaped its enclosure, appeared by the side of the road, happily nibbling grass. Each time, I stopped to try and (yes, you guessed it!) rescue it. Each time, just as I got close enough to pick it up, it would casually hop out of my reach. Recognizing another "sign" when I see one, I dutifully went home, Googled the symbology of rabbits from a spiritual perspective and received the message clearly. By becoming quiet, their inner voice can help guide them to where they need to be. This highly intuitive animal uses her gut to know when it is the right time to take a leap, to spring forward! Quiet that constant mind chatter (not easy for a Gemini!) and listen to that inner voice. This inner guide will give you the confidence you need to take action, take the opportunities, and *leap*. Needless to say, once I got that message, I never saw the little furry tail again. Take the opportunities that were presenting for me, to not hesitate—to *leap*. To stop running around and providing opportunities for others that they were not ready or wanting to take. To embrace fully the new magical events and opportunities that were opening up.

So, I became the lighthouse and the rabbit all at once. Staying still, simply shining—and in that stillness also being ready to leap at the appropriate times—I continue to paddle my canoe strong and sure. Remembering with each stroke of my paddle, my own joyful *Aloha* and gratitude for the journey on my path of wellness. Remembering the wide-eyed joy of that baby photo. Remembering that bowl of light. With a smile, and a deep breath, the phrase that now keeps playing in my head, regarding everyone who I connect with on my journey is: "They get to the beach when they get to the beach."

About the Author

Tracey is a practitioner, teacher, and facilitator who studied a broad spectrum of healing modalities. Providing opportunities for others to clear their path, step into their self-empowerment, and wellness on all levels, she is someone who walks her talk—and, in doing so, inspires others.

Her passion for Hawaiian healing practices, culture, and spirituality, along with her honoring of the wisdom, sacredness, and integrity of the ancient teachings, drives her to spread the Aloha spirit.

http://www.tranceformations.com.au
http://www.alohaspiritaunty.com

Portals of Perfection

———⚬⚬⚬———

Angela Power

Have you ever undertaken the challenge of a rear-view jigsaw puzzle? Already, it sounds difficult, doesn't it? You have to envisage what the picture would look like from the opposite view presented, attempting to complete the task one piece at a time. It's like impatiently looking at the back of someone's head three rows down at the cinema and trying to recognize who they are before the lights go on. If your perspective doesn't shift, then you feel utterly clueless and, for all intents and purposes, working in the dark. The paradox is that I grew up in a world often thwarted by my own disappointments and sometimes got caught up in the *struggle* of *finding solutions* rather than allowing them to flow easily and effortlessly to me.

A typical example was sitting my final nursing exam. With knees knocking, I grappled for answers through the whole ordeal, barely finishing in time. Two weeks later and the result came through in the mail. Upon inspecting the envelope, I found that the crux of my future was reduced to nothing but a teensy weensy piece of shredder-paper, with the inscription in bold type print "FAIL!" Momentarily, I felt like *Alice in Wonderland* falling through the earth, wondering if this was the worst thing ever or if it was just a bad dream. It left me feeling crushed, far from my hopes and dreams. I realized then that I had to change my approach and to stop putting so much pressure on myself.

Better to enjoy each step of the journey knowing
that there is always a choice in everything we do.

A couple of months passed before resitting the exam. During that time, a friend recommended taking up some relaxation classes. It was the perfect time to explore new avenues and create new outcomes. The classes were just what I needed, and I learned how to relax and breathe deeply and calmly. Grounding my thoughts enabled me to manage and organize self-directed study with ease. As the day drew nearer to hitting that *reset* button of resourcefulness, I felt much more in control of my actions. I centered myself with a few deep breaths silently asking for guidance and infusing my mantra that *I had studied hard and knew the answers to the questions.* The moment of truth was when I completed the exam papers with time to spare not only for checking my answers, but also for appreciating and reveling in my newfound *confidence and freedom!*

With achievements come new paths to pursue. I followed my heart's desire and, shortly after gaining my nursing registration in Brisbane, I looked forward to a fresh start enrolled in the postgraduate course offered at the Royal Adelaide Hospital in South Australia. Before long, I was assigned to the haematology ward where patients with blood disorders, particularly Leukemia, were admitted for treatment. I was cognizant of the fact that I would be looking after patients with life-threatening diseases. As a young newly trained nurse, my experiences with death were invariably fleeting, and, in view of that, I felt I would be vulnerable to being thrown in at the deep end. It seemed, therefore, incongruent that I should be so simpatico with patients who would often depart this physical world; yet, concomitantly, I felt beholden to the path of transition that lay before me.

Through a natural desire for enhancing wellbeing, I began to seek out more knowledge regarding vibrational healing. I consequently acquired my very first crystal, a beautiful Brazilian heart-shaped amethyst. I had learned to program it with affirmative thoughts for protection and healing. It came to be a welcome and useful tool not only for me personally, but also for my patients. A thirty-year-old man I was caring for during this time was booked in to have a bronchoscopy for an irritating cough. He felt uneasy and concerned about the procedure. I spoke softly, reassuring him, but I knew he needed further guidance as it wasn't long before he would be whisked away for the medical procedure.

It was at this time that I removed the amethyst from around my neck, handing it to him so that he could familiarize himself with its resonance. I invited him to imagine that he was enveloped by the crystal, breathing calmly, feeling comfortable and protected—completely safe. He held the crystal for a moment, visualizing my instructions, feeling its smoothness, and noticing the clarity it reflected back to him. He thanked me and headed off to undergo the procedure. On his return, he was like an excited child, bright-eyed and brimming with enthusiasm. Elated, he exclaimed, "It worked! It worked!"

Heeding my advice, he allowed himself to let go of all fear and apprehension, drawing only calmness to him. *By focusing on something new, without questioning it, his attention shifted to a place where it had never been before, thus creating a powerful redirection of his own energy and resonance.*

One day, I sat with a young man who was just given the distressing news that following his second round of chemotherapy he had not bounced back into remission. His wife was heavily pregnant with their second child, and this naturally weighed on his mind. I had been caring for him in isolation as this was part and parcel of protecting immunosuppressed patients. I had good rapport with him and had looked after him on and off throughout his treatment regime. I had even loaned him my Walkman to listen to some relaxation tapes. He told me that resting and listening to the tapes made him feel like he was in heaven, far away from his worries and the intrusive procedures that typically occupied each day.

On this particular occasion, while gently cleaning his gums with a jumbo swab, I sensed his pondering gaze upon me. I sat back, looking at him curiously and momentarily tentative, anticipating something poignant about to unfold. He said, pensively, "And I would do that for you too, if you were going to croak." As if captured within an ephemeral void, he smiled *the smile of freedom*, emphatically surrendering to his fate. Reality soon set in as he confided his deepest sorrow, the dispirited thought of leaving his family in such an overwhelming position. His composure was sobering as I replied positively, "If you want to see your baby born, you will!"

While I was on "days off" from shift work, to my surprise, I heard that, despite his feeble condition, the nurses accompanied him to the birth of his second child. They even snapped a photo of "Dad" looking a little worse for wear but happily nursing his newly born baby, and, within a week, he magically transformed his cells to find himself *in remission* from Leukemia; and a short time after, he was given the green light and discharged from hospital. *What is more affirming of life than the joy of birth itself?*

This powerful experience forged within me an awareness of how our reaction to circumstances creates momentum that inevitably portends the actualization of our inescapable future.

Unleashing our grip on the reins opens a portal to what our heart truly desires, and life becomes a cornucopia of wonder and beauty!

These and other defining experiences from my nursing career impressed upon me a deep desire to enhance my skills in holistic healing and, thus inadvertently, became the catalyst for a career path into vibrational therapies. It is no surprise, then, that for over half of my life I have honed my skills and intuition to intentionally relax, align, and soothe others so that they become more open and aware of how they can stay more balanced. Addressing stress through vibrational therapies—such as aromatherapy massage, flower essences, homeopathy, crystal therapy, kinesiology and oriental therapies, and other forms that transform the whole body—is a wonderful way to enjoy a sense of balance. Waiting until you get to hospital and wondering how this illness manifested within you is not the ideal scenario.

When you feel stressed, depressed, confused, or lethargic start by going for a walk in nature, breathing deeply, and letting go of the feeling that is creating the tension or disharmony. Instead, feel the breeze against your cheeks; take in the smell of the outdoors and the sound of the birds. Look closer, and see the windows luminous through the trees. Nurture a tranquil perspective, a lightness of being. With your clarity renewed, choose to feel happy and alive, full of potential! Keep doing this, and you may surprise yourself by noticing that things start to shift and flow positively, enhancing everyday experiences just as you intended. There is a note on my fridge, which has been there for twenty years now, to remind me of the importance of living well and joyfully. Put simply, *everything is perfect!* And so it is!

About the Author

Angela Power has spent over thirty years as a health professional enriched by a career in mostly primary care medical nursing for fifteen years, and as a natural therapist since 1988. For the past twenty years, she has enjoyed servicing the Sunshine Coast Hinterland in Queensland with her successful niche mobile resort massage business, *Touch of Power.* She blends soothing aromatherapy massages with oriental wisdom, rebalancing and educating with intuitive awareness.

http://www.touchofpower.com.au

The Healing Power of Inner Wisdom

Mandy Napier

Life contains gifts often disguised as challenges and adversities that have the potential to transform an ordinary canvas into an amazing life masterpiece. Significant colorful moments, influential events, prominent milestones, when blended together on the palette of our life, define and create the end result: the masterpiece.

Reflecting back on the prominent milestones of my thirties, I see how these sketches have contributed to my life today—my current masterpiece.

- Milestone 1: At thirty, I hung up my well-travelled backpack and dusty walking boots.

- Milestone 2: I got married.

- Milestone 3: I settled in Brisbane, leaving my birthplace, England.

- Milestone 4: I embarked on a successful career in sales and management.

- Milestone 5: At thirty-one, I lined up for my first triathlon. I braved the jelly-fish-infested turbulent ocean. I rode my husband's oversized bike and ran in an old pair of Nike's.

I loved the thrill of racing and physically challenging my body. Placing third in my age group, I became hooked. I've always found that physical challenges build my mental strength, confidence, and courage.

- Milestone 6: At thirty-three. I represented Australia at the world's long course triathlon in Nice, France.

- Milestone 7: At thirty-four, I lined up at Muncie, Illinois, to cross yet another line.

- Milestone 8: At thirty-seven, I competed at the Australian Ironman Championships in Forster and qualified for the Ironman World Championships in Kaluai-Kona, Hawaii, six months later.

I vividly remember the lead up to Forster: the continual long hours of training, the encouraging camaraderie of team mates, and, most importantly, my mental rituals—night after night visualizing running across the finish line. Race day. I remember the cold water swirling through my wetsuit, invading my ears, and seeping into my goggles; the long and lonely energy-sapping bike ride contrasting against the awe inspiring crowds lining the roads of the 42.2 km run; the cheering, unconditional support, fueling me and turbo-charging my performance, helping me pass competitor after competitor; my mantra "You can do it", which I kept repeating; and the elation as I crossed the finish line after ten hours and forty-four minutes—a moment that was forever etched into my mind. Placing third in my age group, I felt strong, confident, and invincible.

Hawaii? Well, it made Forster look like a stroll in the park. Vast open lava fields, shimmering as the Kona winds distorted the heat waves, creating eerie patterns on the horizon. With the added recent injury that could have potentially threatened my race day, the onset of a severe cough, and the secret inner turmoil over my unhappy marriage, I felt vulnerable, fearful, and weak.

A roller coaster of emotions swept over me. *Would my inner fears be revealed on the sacred lava fields of Kona? Could my strong, normally invincible self, fight them off?* There was no going back. I created a mantra for the bike leg: "The wind is my friend." My antidote to the strong winds and to the persistent inner voice that wanted me to quit.

Racking my bike and setting off on the 42.2 km run, I was exhausted and coughing severely. This time, my mantra was focused on surviving: "Every step's a step nearer." Failure was not an option. I kept running, one foot in front of the other, repeating my mantra as the day stretched through sunset into darkness. As I crossed the finish line, exuberance was replaced with relief, and I was grateful to have survived this thirteen-hour ordeal.

I returned home, feeling strangely different, affected by a "spiritual" experience in Hawaii. Watching a sunset over the ocean, I heard a voice saying, "Your spirit is dying. Pay attention and listen. You know what you have to do. Your purpose awaits." On the one hand, it gave me a clear answer to a question that had plagued me for too long, yet it also opened unanswered questions I had held since childhood. Why are we here and what is my purpose?

- Milestone 9: I left my marriage after years of emotional upheaval. I had no home and no family in Australia. I was in debt, yet I felt lightness in my being. I qualified for Forster again and set my sights on returning to Hawaii, my Everest, to give it one more crack, preferring to focus on what I loved rather than having to face other areas of my life that needed serious attention. I blocked out the hurt, hoping it would go away.

- Milestone 10: Three months short of my thirty-eighth birthday, my world fell apart. Almost overnight, I had to stop running. I had been experiencing unexplained muscle spasms when I ran, and now they literally stopped me in my tracks. It was as if my body was saying, "Hey, listen to me." I sought help from a variety of health professionals. No one had an answer.

I was in pain, confused, and lost, and unable to train. Feeling angry, frustrated, and weak, internal battles raged inside my mind. I had literally used "running" to run away from my unhappy marriage, my pain. As I had become fitter and stronger in body, my ability to resolve my personal dilemma diminished. I shoved my

112

emotions down, locking them into my body. You cannot function well on the outside when you choose not to pay attention to your internal world. I reflected on Hawaii, the race, the voice from the ocean, my life, and my future. Somehow, I knew I held the keys to my recovery, which would open up a brand new palette of colors.

As I asked myself some tough questions, I started to accept my situation. My healing began when I forgave myself for staying in an unhappy marriage for so long and when I made friends with my tortured body, as I had done with the elements in Hawaii. I stopped fighting what I couldn't change, and surrendered. Knowing I could no longer hide, I enrolled in a ten-day retreat, where it was time to face my fears. As I learned about myself, working from the inside out, I began to shed my baggage. Past emotions, thoughts, and memories tumbled out.

My heart began to open, letting the warm sunlight shine in as my winter turned to spring. Slowly, my body started to heal, and my spirit started to shine again.

I continued attending courses and seminars where I discovered hidden patterns. I broke bonds of loyalty, obligation, and duty, childhood beliefs that chained me to a desperately unhappy marriage. I transformed the seeds of „not good enough" and released a deep fear of abandonment, reshaping my inner world.

- Milestone 11: In my thirty-ninth year, on an ordinary Monday morning, I was drawn, as if by some magical spell, to my favorite coffee shop. Little did I know how this decision would fill my canvas with a gigantic splash of vibrant color.

It was as if the Universe conspired for this moment to happen. In walked a man I knew—my future and current husband. As we greeted each other, a flash of joyful light ignited the air, sending warm electric shivers through my body. I knew I had met my soul mate.

As the saying goes, the rest is history. We married in a private game reserve in Africa to the sounds of the African bush, hippos, elephants, and a cacophony of birds, accompanied by a beautiful female leopard magically appearing in front of our jeep.

We moved to the Sunshine Coast, and the pieces of the puzzle came together. I understood the message from Hawaii. A light bulb moment illuminated the way forward, and I knew exactly what I had to do. I left a successful career and established Mindset for Success, combining years of learning from travel, sports, and the thousands of hours of training and courses with the powerful mind tools that helped me transform my life and color my world.

Today, I live my passion, coaching and assisting people to harness the power of their minds. Aligning their unconscious and conscious minds, I teach them how to use these transformational tools. Weekend warriors, Ironmen and women, athletes, business professionals, and everyday people trapped in their past patterns, creating winning strategies, rituals, and healthy habits for living healthier, happier lives.

Today, my life has a sense of balance. I still love to exercise, preferring shorter distances to Ironman races. Yoga has become an integral part of my life, and I have the unconditional love of my amazing husband. I am living my purpose, and I feel wiser and complete.

When you are dealing with real life issues, you need to stop and to trust and look at yourself. Your internal conflicts reflect issues of misalignment, values, meaning, identity, purpose, and connection. When you align and harness the power of your mind, magic happens. When you stop resisting and start accepting and trusting where and who you are, while being open to receive the gifts that await, your life will flourish again. Bodies heal, relationships flourish, soul mates are found, and passions reignited or discovered.

Life contains gifts that, if you are open to receive, have the potential to transform an ordinary life into an extraordinary one. Here are a few pieces of wisdom that helped me create my masterpiece:

- Keep on learning.

- Be curious and open-minded.

- Get to know yourself intimately.

- Accept what you can't change, and only change what you can.

- Be free of judgment. It minimizes your power.

- Love and believe in yourself.

- Maintain a balance in your life.

- Never ever give up on yourself.

- In the words of Pema Chödrön, „Nothing ever goes away until it has taught us what we need to know."

Only then, as Buddha said, „Like the moon, come out from behind the clouds! Shine."

About the Author

Mandy Napier BSC (Hons), dubbed the Mindset Alchemist, has helped thousands of clients to clear their blocks and self-sabotaging patterns through her proprietary CLEAR coaching system. Having broken through her own mental barriers while competing in ultra distance triathlons and discovering powerful, transformational tools that helped her heal her life, Mandy coaches people on how to align and harness the power of their minds to perform optimally and live happier, healthier lives.

http://www.mindsetforsuccess.com.au

The Gift of Yoga

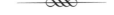

Susan Deakin

We are only one breath away from life or death. I remember when I was a child my mum telling me, "We naturally breathe about twenty thousand times a day without even thinking, but until I learned to appreciate and value my breath, I was able to find the courage and strength I needed to make the changes in my life that I couldn't except, except what I couldn't change, and slowly work toward becoming the person I always wanted to be." From the age of fifteen, I felt lost. I wasn't sure what I wanted to do with my life, and I worried too much about my future. I was a free spirit and often felt like I disappointed my parents, as I didn't always do or act how they wanted me to. This made it hard to accept the person I was because, through trying to please others, I was neglecting my own needs and wants and losing the respect of the people I was trying to please.

I think Mum would remember the exact day I changed. She said my schoolbooks were always neat and tidy. All of a sudden, I stopped caring. I left home at the age of eighteen and lived on Queensland's Gold Coast for a couple of years, working as a bar maid at a popular hotel called Fisherman's Wharf. I saved enough money working there before heading off to America. I spent the next three years traveling and sailing the globe. During this time, I worked as a housemaid cleaning million-dollar apartments in Keystone, Colorado, and used my friendliest Aussie accent to help earn me big tips waitressing in America and in an English pub in London. I also became a stewardess on several super yachts in the

Mediterranean, picked fruit and flowers on a farm in Israel, and sailed across the Atlantic Ocean from Gibraltar to the Caribbean on a 110-foot traditional sailing yacht for over one month—arriving at Antigua on Christmas Day.

This period of my life taught me many valuable life lessons. There were times during my travels when I wasn't in control and had to learn faith, accept reality as it was, and accept the unknown. When I needed money, I always found work. Difficult situations always worked out in the end. And when I was crossing the Atlantic Ocean in a vicious squall in the middle of the night, I knew that I wasn't meant to die.

After three years of a free and easy life, I heard the whispers in my heart saying, "It is time to go home and get some stability in my life. My childhood dream was to find a wonderful man, have children, and live a happy, healthy life." I was home for only one day and my youngest sister, fifteen at the time, and I decided to go to Brampton Island on a day cruise. This trip changed the direction of my life and steered me in the arms of a man who became my husband and father to our three beautiful daughters.

I learned the power of thought! Be careful what you wish for, as dreams do come true!

During our married life, we owned and operated eight businesses in eight different industries over a span of twenty years. A health and fitness centre, upmarket cafés, mortgage finance, and a multi million-dollar property development business. We worked so hard that we forgot to feel, sense, and know life moment by moment. Our life lacked meaning. We had everything we needed but were working for bigger houses, better cars, and more materialistic things that were creating more stress on us and not making us any happier.

This period of our life was the catalyst that helped change our perspective on what was important to us. We wanted a better quality of life, not quantity. So within six weeks, we packed up the family and our Great Dane, Tiny, put our finance business under management, and headed off to the land of the Great White Cloud to live.

Within a few weeks of arriving, I signed up for a two-year full-time extensive Yoga teacher training course at Auckland Yoga Academy. I had practiced Yoga before and knew it was more than just a physical practice; it tapped into something else: the internal, the breath. I wanted to learn this timeless wisdom that could help me find lasting happiness and bring peace and harmony to my mind and body. I committed to five days a week Ashtanga Yoga practice, slowly working through the primary and secondary series of the Ashtanga sequence over a period of two years. My daily practice also included breathing exercises and meditation practice. In the beginning, I was tired from pushing so hard to perfect every pose. I grew up as a competitive solo athlete and competed at state swimming events for a lot of my childhood and in my early twenties in triathlon events throughout the state. This was high-intensity training, and in the beginning I treated my Yoga practice in the same way.

I remember one day I was trying so hard to get my chin to the floor in Baddha Konasana, a hip opening pose of the primary series, that my teacher whispered quietly in my ear, "Just be happy you have two arms and two legs." This little message was the start of me learning real Yoga. I learned to listen to my body and adjust my Yoga practice to how I was feeling on any particular day. Some days I would float beautifully through my practice, and the next day I would stumble and struggle to find balance. I learned to accept where I was in the present moment and accept that my emotion, what I ate, how much I slept, all contributed to this feeling of flow and balance.

Yoga is not competitive in any way. It's primarily about mindfulness and learning to live in the present moment. Patanjali, who compiled the Yoga Sutras, defines Yoga as the ability to direct the mind exclusively toward an object and sustain focus in that direction without distractions. As I breathe through my daily Yoga practice, I focus on my breath to release tension in my body and my mind. I release what no longer serves me and send my breath wherever it is needed. Now, as I perceive pain and discomfort, I breathe deeply as I send healing to the area that is struggling. I am amazed of how it works every time. Life force energy flows within every cell of our being. We can send it to wherever it is needed.

In 2013, we moved back to Australia to be closer to our family. I opened a Yoga studio and named the studio 8 Limb Yoga, as I was committed to teach the 8 limbs of Yoga: the first two limbs relate to life principles that promote us to bring non-harm to ourselves and others and that encourage us to be more supportive, more compassionate, and kinder to others and ourselves in the world; one limb relates to Asana practice—the physical postures to improve strength, flexibility, and balance in the body; one limb relates to different breathing techniques to enhance life-force energy to the body and mind; and the last four limbs relate to meditation practice.

Many people balk at the word meditation, but just sitting in stillness for a few minutes each day brings so many positive effects on our health and happiness. A meditative experience is no different then experiencing similar feelings of drifting . . . slowly awake and laying there in a delicious restfulness, or feeling the utter wonder and vastness of the night sky. These are spontaneous experiences typically lasting for a few seconds to a few minutes. Meditative awareness is no different, but it is intentional. This message I often share to my students in my Yoga class is of an old Cherokee talking with his grandson: "My son, there is a battle between two wolves inside us all. One is Evil. It is anger, jealousy, greed, resentment, inferiority, lies, and ego. The other is Good. It is joy, peace, love, hope, humility, kindness, empathy, and truth." The little boy thought about it for a while and asked, "Grandfather, which wolf wins?" The old man quietly replied, "The one you feed."

There is no better gift to give your family and friends than the best of yourself.

I will be forever grateful to my parents; my husband and friend for his constant encouragement and support; our three beautiful daughters who make us so proud and bring us so much joy and happiness; and for the Gift of Yoga, which has helped me to find peace and happiness in my heart.

I now feel, more so than ever before, that I owe my fortunate life to the improvement of others and contributing to the world. Om Shanti Shanti Shanti.

About the Author

Susan Deakin completed an intensive teaching training course at Auckland Yoga Academy under Jude Hynes, a student of the late Pattabhi Jois who is the founder of Ashtanga Yoga. She is co-owner of 8 Limb Yoga studio in Mackay where she teaches Yoga and is the lead trainer for Teacher Training. Susan has owned many successful businesses with her husband of twenty-two years and has three teenage daughters that she is most proud of.

http://www.8limbyoga.com.au

Transformation . . . From Pain to Joy

Donna McCormick

My path in this life has been to develop and grow and also serve others—just like many of you reading this book. And I've learned some simple foundational tenets that allow all of us to transform and develop and build a bridge from pain of any type to live a life of peace and joy.

Let me share these five tenets with you as I show my life and the path I now live to help others heal themselves and manifest their own joyous lives.

I was fortunate to be gifted into a stable family environment with a twin brother and two other brothers. The blessings of great parents, strong business ethics, and a traditional lifestyle in a middle class family on the north shore of Sydney seemed like the perfect start; but I was different, no matter what I tried to do.

I was the blond little daughter trying to be the good girl, and I was blessed with seeing "truths" in others and situations. I had the gift of honesty that often delivered raw blunt truth, which I thought was "normal" because I thought everyone saw the world as I did—very clearly—with all the nuances of shadow and light. So I struggled that others didn't see this world like I did, as I was frequently misunderstood and often hurt, and became very sensitive to the point of feeling that I didn't seem to belong.

With the gift of adult hindsight, I know now that I also had dyslexia, but I thought that was normal and that I was just slow—so

I learned to hide the fact that I couldn't focus at school, that reading was beyond difficult for me, and that writing something could take hours. I felt I was at fault, and quickly learned strategies to cover and hide even more.

As time progressed, during my teenage years, I continued learning to cover and mask my faults (and really my soul and joy) in being unable to fit in with others. I appeared to be the "social butterfly" and the life of the party, while internally I felt empty, lost, and disconnected. I trusted everyone. And though I could at times seem to be naïve, I was always able to see into people's souls— their pain, their troubles as well as their potential. As a result, I have always been able to hold empathy and compassion and to be totally forgiving. But I thought everyone could see and do that too, and I didn't understand the confusion, hostility, and aggression in this world.

Frequently, I surrendered my personal power to belong, and often attracted some toxic relationships that served to teach me some of my greatest lessons. My first marriage gave me the gift of two amazing sons who are my greatest joys and teachers.

My second marriage reinforced my habit of self-sacrifice to provide a perceived need for another father figure for my boys. But, with the gift of hindsight once again, he blessed me with the circumstances of control to harness my joy, and I finally learned to stand up and own both my choices and the consequences of that false "mask".

After so many years of trying too hard to fit in and feel safe and secure, I had turned into a harmonizer and rescuer to the extreme. I was a super-doer-fixer woman and corporate achiever, and I strove to be a great mother as well as an over-the-top house-keeper to serve all those I loved. . . .

As can be expected, eventually, I broke down.

Dis-ease won: glandular fever, chronic fatigue syndrome, poly-cystic ovaries. And, ultimately, I progressed to fibromyalgia. Then, realizations really started to hit me.

I'd spent a life forgiving others and apologizing for who I was, always trying and struggling to fit in; but I'd never spent time loving and forgiving myself for owning my own uniqueness and letting myself just be me!

I had to live the lessons myself and take the universal hits of dis-ease to a place of full forgiveness to heal.

Courage was needed. I became determined to heal myself and transform my own life and live with true authenticity. With that frame of mind, the option of alternative medicine was shown to me . . . and the path to wellness and living joyously began.

As I discovered, the first tenet of a transformed life is *complete* forgiveness of yourself—your doubts, your misgivings, your judgments of yourself and others. This is not new, but to truly surrender to the depths of forgiveness takes courage; it means letting go of our egoic stories, and a trust that there's a greater path for you and me to follow.

Over the next five years, I immersed myself with healings and alternative therapies as I looked deeper and spent the time to honor myself with greater self-care. Much like yourself, some healings and therapists resonated with me, and some did not. While holding self-forgiveness in my core, I further developed my inner sense and trust to know my mind, body, and soul implicitly.

The next three tenets were honed during these years and are the foundations to live by at all times: Love, Respect, and Kindness.

Apply these tenets to yourself, to others, and to every situation *at all times.* In any moment of stress or decision making, take a moment to breathe in forgiveness, remind yourself of Love, Respect, and Kindness, and then choose your response.

As I healed and honored myself while applying these tenets to my own life, I built my own toolkit and realized that healing and teaching are my natural calling.

Eventually, my own healing and the release of all dis-ease enabled me to continue my transformation, and so I resigned from the traditional lifestyle and corporate career pathway. Eleven years ago, I fully opened my heart to who I really am—to be truly of service to humanity as a facilitator of transformation and love. I founded my own business, Spectrum Healing and Teaching, and I've had the privilege of facilitating over 20,000 sessions with beautiful souls willing to transform and live more authentically.

They now call me the Teacher of the Teachers, I am the facilitator of transformation and expansion, and I share my story openly to show you that anything is possible and that the following tenets will serve your own path to create a life you love:

1. Forgiveness

2. Love

3. Respect

4. Kindness

These first four will help you develop an even greater sense for the fifth tenet:

5. Gratitude

Gratitude is often spoken of as the great panacea for all ills. To a degree, any sense of gratitude will help, but it's when the first four are developed, explored, and lived that the fullest sense of gratitude can be felt and can resonate throughout your life and experiences.

All five tenets will build to greater depths within you; together, they will deliver even more joy into your life. With more joy comes more gratitude, and with more gratitude comes more joy.

As for me now, well I've seen and lived the dangers of living inauthentically. My path has helped me heal myself and helped me serve thousands of others. I am completely free of all dis-ease in my body and, as a reward, I have become an energetic DNA and endocrine specialist. I'm also passionate in honoring the divine feminine, which interweaves into all my work for both yin and yang. I develop and write workshops; support other along their healing path; create amazing meditations; and have a strong, busy, abundant spiritual practice and business.

I live a whole and complete life in every facet. I also have full faith and trust in myself and our Universe. I love my life, and I live with these five tenets daily. I'm so grateful for every experience this crazy world has thrown at me to live my joyous life to help and inspire others in doing the same.

Hold true to these five tenets, and manifest the life you desire with joy.

Always with Love, Respect, and Kindness. . . .

About the Author

Donna McCormick is a multi-dimensional spectrum healer, with an open conscious channel working directly with your spirit, mind, body, soul, and energetic system. She facilitates transformation and expansion to help you understand and heal your blockages and fears to give you the clarity, truth, and awareness to live more fully and to actualize your potential.

Donna has had the honor and privilege of having facilitated over 20,000 healing and mentoring sessions—healing and teaching with Love, Respect, and Kindness.

http://www.spectrumhealing.com.au

Spiritual Teacher

---∞∞∞---

Maria de Cinque

At fifteen, I was working as a dress maker for a fashion designer. Father had no money to support my studies, so I worked in a drug store and studied beauty therapy and remedial massage at night school. I made my own wax and ran to people's homes to wax their legs.

While I was working in the drug store, Mum got Leukemia. When I was seventeen, I met my husband-to-be, whom I didn't like enough to marry. My Italian family stamped their communal foot and insisted that he was a good man. Father threw an enormous engagement party, believing Mum wouldn't make it to the wedding. He was right. She died on Mother's Day the year I turned eighteen.

I overheard my father weeping and saying he didn't know what to do with me. The last thing I wanted to do was to be married to a man I barely knew. Mum's passing bought me time to grieve, but not enough. The night before our wedding, my husband-to-be and I had an enormous argument and decided not to marry. When we told everyone, I couldn't believe it. I went into shock and slept between by brother and his wife for two weeks.

Three months later, we went through with the wedding. It was the only way to get out of the house, away from my controlling father, whom I loved, unlike my husband-to-be. I built my business up from nothing. When doing facials, I saw images of people's lives and got messages from Spirit, and I'd communicate these messages to them.

Stunned, they would ask, "How do you know this?"

I thought everyone could do it. After massaging people, they commented, "You have healing hands." I would release their pain, but I was always curious about the *actual source*.

It was starting to occur to me that I was a spiritual healer and teacher, but my area of expertise was to teach people beauty therapy and massage, so that's where it began. . . .

Our first son was born, and finally I had someone to love for three months straight without having to work. Being a mother assuaged the pain of losing one a little bit. . . .

I was a mother, a successful business woman, a teacher, and only twenty-four. I owned my beauty clinic and school of beauty and massage. I was passionate about my work and started branching into Reiki and advanced Pranic healing, just in time for the birth of our second son, who was breast-fed while I read books on Chinese medicine, acupuncture, and spiritual energy medicine. The baby was ravenous, and so was I for healing techniques. The marriage went by the wayside, where it should have stayed, and we divorced.

I just kept working day and night; teaching; and running between beauty therapy, day care, and my first son's school. On weekends, sometimes my sisters would mind the boys so I could go to the gym and get a massage. There, I met my lover, who fathered my third son and who became my business partner and loving soul mate.

Four months before the birth of my third son, my soul mate was called overseas on mysterious business. We wrote long-hand every week, until the day a typed letter arrived, and I knew it was over. Another devastating loss at thirty-three, while carrying our unborn child. . . .

Heart-broken, I worked and breastfed at work—and my staff doubled as aunties, until I burned out and sold the business, and I kept teaching, knowing in my heart I would always love the father of this love child, even though I feared I would never see him again. . . .

My deepest need was to heal the many physical ailments which started surfacing within my body, but all of my focus was on others, my boys, and learning—so much new learning to fill the void. I studied naturopathy and nutrition, became a raw food coach, and worked out that people's ailments, including my own, could not be healed by naturopathy alone. There had to be more. . . .

127

By the time my youngest son was three, I met a medical student, whom I supported at my house until he graduated. He was charming, spontaneous, and made me laugh. For more than a decade, that was enough.

I started new businesses with my new husband. We bought a franchise hair transplant clinic and, after twelve months, I added cosmetic medicine and a surgery. I realized the psychology of the human mind through what appearances mean to people—papering over sometimes unacknowledged interior pain with exterior cosmetic work.

Twelve years into that marriage, we divorced and sold the clinic. I turned to studying mediumship, finally understanding the mysterious "soul whisperer" messages I received from the start, as early as when waxing people's legs in my teens. Ever hungry for learning, I became an NLP practitioner, all without truly understanding that my drive for healing and knowledge was heading not outward but inward to analytical psychology.

After four decades of searching, I found ThetaHealing ®.

ThetaHealing® took me to a whole new realm of understanding about how to seek and work on the origin of the belief or illness. It's about getting the client into a theta state, where I can assist them heart to heart with the spiritual guidance given to me by The Creator. We're talking about the healing energy of all that is. We all come from the same fabric, different weaves/histories and behavioral patterns, and theta healing shifts the source of beliefs that makes us ill and no longer serves us.

After four decades of healing others, I realized it was time to heal me.

I recalled a past life regression I did back in the eighties that I never knew how to heal.

I was in a workshop and took my turn to lie on the table. The teacher asked if there was any pain in my body.

I said, "I occasionally feel pain in my pelvic region, but doctors had never found the cause."

The teacher asked permission to journey with me with his guidance. I connected to the feeling of my pain. I saw darkness, and, in a whirlpool of movement, a tunnel appeared. My heart was beating so fast in my ears. The turbulence felt like my heart valves snapped shut. I couldn't see myself, but I remember the emotions linked to the experience. I was so scared, I was falling deeper and deeper into the dark tunnel. My little heart kept fighting to stay, to stop this. My instinctive, immediate reaction to danger was that I was going to disappear into nothing. My pain was excruciating. I was fighting for life. I was being swallowed.

Back on the table in the workshop, I felt like I was going to have a panic attack. I heard a voice—the teacher asking where I was.

"I am in my Mother's womb."

"What's happening?"

"They don't want me."

"Who don't want you?"

"Mum and Dad. This pain I'm feeling, is it my mother's birth pain, or is it my own birth pain?"

I was crying so much, sourcing enormous sadness, desperation, rejection, being unwanted, not loved, and abandonment terror.

"Why don't they want you?" the teacher asked me.

"I don't know. Mum is having problems with me, and I want to stay with her. They can't just get rid of me! I'm here for a reason! How can this be happening to me?" My heart was so heavy with pain that I felt it was breaking to bits. I was exhausted, but I knew I couldn't give up—I was not ready to die.

After the teacher completed the journey with me, I was so shocked to know I had been through this trauma. I knew I had won my battle for survival, but *why?*

A few years later, I went to visit my father in a home. Noticing that he was looking strangely at me, I asked, "Why are you staring at me like that?"

"You are so different to the others, so beautiful."

I was surprised. Compliments were not really my father.

"You know when your mother was pregnant with you, she was very sick, we thought she's going to die. The doctor gave her tablets to abort you, but you were a fighter—you held on."

I was shocked and speechless. I stared at him in astonishment. He then began to cry, purging long suppressed fear, guilt, and remorse. This stimulated his anger to punish himself through years of suppression. . . . My father said he was also disappointed when I was born because he wanted a boy. I was devastated by this news. Another punch in the gut!

He was still crying when I realized this was his way of asking me for forgiveness. I saw how relieved he felt for having the courage to tell me. I just occupied the space for his confession. I remember this well of peace formed between us. He left his resentment and guilt behind. During that week, my father's words replayed in my head. My healing was done in the past life regression, the pain had gone, but I still had the residue of some beliefs inside of me. This was playing up in my relationships: mistrust, not feeling safe, etc.

Remembering the regression and putting the two together was like a miracle. The missing pieces were found for me to have the realization and confirmation of my truth. I thank my father for sharing this with me, as this has healed us both.

Theta healing gave me back the untraumatized silence and sanctuary of my mother's womb before I entered the consciousness of humans.

About the Author

Maria de Cinque combines science and spirituality, intuitively connecting with the phenomenal self of her clients. She works heart to heart to unveil their soul's purpose with passion as a wellness leader. As a certified ThetaHealing® Energy Medicine Instructor and Practitioner, Maria, allows people to consciously create their holographic universe with the energy of "All That Is", repairing core fractures, cleaning toxic emotions, and shifting restrictions on a cellular level.

http://www.thetahealingheart.com.au
http://www.mariadecinque.com

The Healing Power of
Honoring Our Humanity

Kate Moody

My CFS Story

For fifteen years, I lived a ceaselessly busy life, driven by a constant need to achieve and a tireless commitment to my corporate profession. I had lived a good part of my life actively pursuing my life goals and being physically fit. For over a decade, I had been constantly pushing myself beyond my limits on all levels and overriding the need to listen to my body for rest and nourishment.

In 2010, my many years of "burning the candle at both ends" finally caught up with me when I became debilitated with Chronic Fatigue Syndrome (CFS). My body was often in a state of "fight or flight" mode, with the pressures and deadlines of a corporate career. Toward the end of my career in 2009, I started to suffer severe lower back pain and burnout. I consequently suffered symptoms such as glandular fever, epstein-barr virus, intolerances to foods, a constant sore throat, swollen glands, muscle weakness and pain, and then debilitating chronic fatigue. This resulted in my life turning upside down. I experienced grief in the letting-go process of losing my "independence" identity at the peak of my youth at just thirty-one years. I felt betrayal toward my body and life as I once knew it. I withdrew from the world in solitude to consciously heal my body, mind, and energy system for two and a half years.

The fatigue was absolutely devastating and overwhelming. For twelve months, a heavy blanket of exhaustion, lethargy, and grief pressed down on me. I began to experience short-term memory loss, the loss of my personal will and motivation, and an inability to organize my mind and life. Virtually overnight, I went from being superwoman to being bedridden 24/7 for six months. The acute stage of CFS was a very raw, vulnerable, and painful experience on all levels.

I tried to keep my illness away from my family and friends so as not to be a burden and a negative impact on them. A lot of my suffering, anxiousness, and grieving involved "holding in" or keeping it to myself. Often, it was in the shower where I allowed myself to fall apart and collapse into an emotional breakdown and to just be with how awful I was feeling through my body. It was as if this was my moment to be alone, and be with the rawness of my vulnerability, as the rush of the water drowned out my cathartic grieving and soothed my aching and feeble body. It was a time I could let go of my apparent strong exterior front, of holding it together and appearing okay on the outside to others. This was the internal process of being broken open, the ego collapsing and leaving me with no choice but to surrender into the rawness and unknown healing journey.

My internal and external world was shattered, and now a new paradigm of internal values, beliefs, and love needed to emerge for the recovery process.

The Healing Journey Begins With Acceptance and Surrender

Each step of my healing journey was very intuitive and involved several turning points for rebuilding my life.

Life lived with this illness meant I had to change, and I needed to recognize that change is not always a bad thing. Acceptance was a major step toward feeling better and toward recovery. Acceptance doesn't only mean embracing your pain or identifying yourself only as a person with the illness of CFS, but it also means a willingness to experience pain and fatigue as a part of life, and a willingness to move on with your life even when pain and fatigue are present.

132

Listening to the Body Wisdom

Learning to listen to the wisdom of my body was another significant step toward recovery. I discovered that the moment you start to truly listen to your body, you send a powerful message to your brain, and your body stops resisting the healing process. I had to break the pattern of pushing myself too hard by honestly looking at my need to achieve and to be "always doing". The more I began listening to the messages my body was sending me, the more I stopped fighting the symptoms and allowed my body to completely rest and be still. Consequently, I slowly started to improve.

Humans have the extraordinary ability to choose the meaning of their experiences. You can make a conscious choice to let your pain and illness lead you to greater clarity and insight and to allow the experience to make you wiser and stronger.

Being able to truly relax and rest my body brought huge benefits to me. It enabled me to rebuild a relationship between myself and my body—learning to befriend my body and suffering, and listening to the language of its wisdom.

Learning to pace myself was a real challenge as I had to change a lifetime of faulty core-beliefs and thought patterns. I believe this was partly linked to my (then) low self-esteem and patterns I had learned during childhood. With CFS, I had to learn a new way of being in the world.

Honoring the Grieving Process

The grieving process is a difficult and painful, but necessary, reaction to any significant loss. My grieving process took place over twelve months. Healing and recovery cannot take place until the loss is mourned.

These were the stages I identified as part of my grieving process: denial, anger, sadness, depression (for some), and acceptance/ adaptation.

We may experience the stages in order, skip around them, omit certain stages entirely if we're not ready to face that part, or return to one stage repeatedly. There is no right way to grieve, nor an easy one.

Grieving and rebuilding allow new strengths and perceptions to emerge.

Grief is part of coming to terms with a new reality, when there is a significant loss experienced. There is no timeframe around the process of grief. You will heal, and you will rebuild yourself around the loss you have suffered. You will be whole again, but you will never be the same. Nor would you want to be.

The Recovery Process

One of the keys to my recovery was surrounding myself with the company of people who would uplift my spirits. Unfortunately, I did have to let go of friends and connections who constantly judged and misunderstood where I was at in life. At the time, it was painful to let go of these friendships but very necessary for my recovery. I became grateful for the little things and worried less about the things I could not change. I found myself leaving behind the history of yesterday and discerning how I would use today's energy to bring about healing and nourishment into my day.

Rebirthing a New Way of Being

Restoring my life force and rebuilding my life over the last four years have made me realize just how precious my energy and time on this planet really are. It has made me more discerning in where and how I place my energy with people and situations. Being true and authentic to you, your precious time, and energy are the greatest gifts you can give to your wellbeing and the relationships around you!

As I am birthing my vision for Radiant Wellbeing in Melbourne, Australia, I feel truly blessed to have come through the other side of CFS—now that the illness no longer affects my overall wellbeing. It is truly wonderful to again feel such an aliveness of peace, joy, and vitality running through my cells and body. I feel like I have been given a second chance at life, to live and love fully with compassion and in gratitude for everything that has been, is, and will be.

Living a life of radiant wellbeing now gives me a sense of deep gratitude for what I have been through over the last four years. I have realized that every crossroad and transformation in my life offers a gift and opening to the next chapter in my life.

An illness, chronic condition, or life-changing circumstance is a "wake up call" in your life. It offers the opportunity for the healing process to return you to a place of wholeness, wellbeing, love, and true self-expression. Within each of us, there is a core: our essence and original self. It is the purpose of our lives to find our essence and our birthright to express our true nature. Even our most painful experiences in life can serve that purpose through deeply learning how to love ourselves unconditionally.

As part of our collective survival as a human race, we need love and connection. The essential survival factor for a human being is love. Love is what promotes wellness for an individual and acceptance and compassion between two human beings.

May you come to know who you truly are within the heart of your healing journey—back to wholeness, love, and radiant wellbeing. May your journey of empowerment to your greatness always be guided by the wisdom of your heart and body, feelings, intuition, and grace.

About the Author

Kate Moody is the founder of Radiant Wellbeing in Melbourne, Australia. She is a Yoga teacher and trainer, specializing in the restoration of health and empowerment for women. She is also involved in prenatal work and has created her own specialized women's Yoga teacher training course.

Kate has a passion for using her experiences of illness and her subsequent recovery and healing journey as a tool to empower others for restoring radiant wellbeing.

http://www.radiantwellbeing.com.au

How the Embodiment of Flow Saved My Life

Alysa Huppler-Poliak

You never know who you are going to meet or how they are going to transform your life. I believe that everything, every person, every decision happens for a reason. For most of my life, I lived as a scared and fear-driven girl. I feared not having clarity or true focus or dedication to my passions, hopes, and dreams. My future, until recently, was unclear and without direction. I did not understand that what is important is not just life's destination, but the journey to get there.

But to fully understand my story, I need to take you even further back, to my childhood.

I nearly died twice before the age of ten: first, a premature birth of three months, and then a life in an incubator. On February 15, 1996, my world changed forever. I didn't know the reason at the time of why I survived, when my mom and I were T-Boned by a semi truck on the Trans-Canada Highway. My fragile body was drawn out of the passenger seat of our 1987 Toyota Tercel by the Jaws of Life. The result was a young girl with a severe frontal lobe injury, in a coma that she would stay in for ten days, with the left side of her body in paralysis for two and a half weeks. No one—not the doctors nor the neurology team—thought I would ever live at full capacity. Thus, the road to recovery was not easy. I fought long and hard, relearning how to walk and talk, redeveloping my memory, and managing my emotions.

Years later, in early 2013, I was living an amazing life, in one of the most beautiful places in the world, in Santa Barbara, California, and I was going to the number one city college in America, yet I was so empty and alone inside. It was here that my massive depression set in, with a miss diagnosis of bipolar II, I became a young person walking a fine line between life and death. I found myself with my hands around my neck, convulsing; I felt so alone in this world and saw no light at the end of the tunnel. I remember thinking to myself, "If something doesn't change, I don't think I am going to make it to thirty." This was my true turning point, as I felt death and darkness at my core. It was this realization that brought me back to my hometown in Canada for a summer of healing and support!

That summer in Canada started out rough. The ruts in my neural pathways had become so deep and massively entangled that nothing could stop my negative thinking. This was not until my mom introduced me to a young couple, Lara Berg and Kevin Heidt, who had recently moved to our town with their Sunshine Yoga Project.

Through this relationship, my life began to transform.

We developed a life-long friendship that summer. This was the first of many synchronistic developments; here, my sympathetic nervous system gave way to me, cultivating the DNA of my true life's blueprint.

The second of these events was introduced to me by Lara—it was called Awesomeness Fest. This event brings together heart-centered entrepreneurs, authors, life coaches, and speakers, all who want to push humanity forward. It was far more amazing than anything I had ever experienced before. It was the global family and community of change makers that I had always wanted. During the last session, lead by transformational coach Lisa Nichols, is where I embodied my vision. As she spoke on the topic of "using the adversities of ones past to create their own destiny", I realized I wanted to inspire, motivate, and help people transform their lives through connecting with my struggles and story of my own transformation and what I was becoming.

After leaving Awesomeness Fest, I was off to Israel to visit family. Little did I know that soon after I arrived I would complete a facilitator certification of the Passion Test, created by Janet

Attwood—an experience that was directly associated with my vision of being a servant leader. In the past, I would have said, "No, it's OK; it is too expensive." However, in life, we often need to take leaps of faith and invest in ourselves. I knew I wanted to work with young people and help them find clarity and direction in their lives. I realized that, globally, the education system was broken. That there was a missing link of transformational education. I made the intention, then and there, that by the time I was thirty (now with the belief that I'd reach that age), I would have helped integrate personal growth, live vision planning, passion exploration, and social entrepreneurial development into the system.

The Passion Test is a major reason my life has turned out the way it has. January 16, 2013, I was aboard a United flight from Orlando to LAX, where I met a man named Louis Berk. It may have been the Star of David around his neck that caught my attention first, but to this day we both say this is the best relationship either of us had ever developed—and on a plane for that matter! He asked me what I did, and I said, "I work in purpose and passion exploration." He felt the connection! He introduced me to a group he works with, a revolutionary scientific breakthrough company called Qivana. A company whose mission is to be best, not the biggest—just the best company in scientific breakthroughs in natural products. By finding the world's leading scientists in an area where there is a critical need, Qivana brings scientific breakthrough products that are not only endorsed by doctors, but that are also developed by them to the market. A purpose-driven company, they help consumers transform their health holistically, by working at the cellular level and fixing the root of their problems.

Right away, I was intrigued. *Combining science and natural products? Ingenious!* Unfortunately, the timing was off as I was just about to go on an around-the-world journey. However, I decided to take a leap of faith! I became an independent business owner with Qivana, and took it with me to spread the company worldwide.

On August 6, 2014, ten countries and nine months later, I was in a rice field in Ubud, Bali. I was being called state-side; however, I intended to return to my home in Malaysia. I made a plan to go to Nevada for another festival called Burning Man.

Eight days later, bam! I had manifested a ticket. I wanted to spend a few weeks in California, reconnecting with friends and family, and then go to Orlando for the Qivana Convention, knowing that if I didn't, I would never really know what I had been given. In the end, I did it all.

When I flew from San Diego to Orlando on September 15, 2014, I knew this would be a transformational weekend for me. I had traveled the world while working on ten different projects and I had put very little effort into Qivana. I knew either Qivana and I would align—and my whole heart and soul would go into it—or I would let go of it for good. Long story short, as fate would have it, I never returned abroad, as I had such a deep connection with the founders, leaders, and people at this convention, which reminded me of Awesomeness Fest. If there were ever a team of movers, shakers, and transformational leaders, it would be Qivanas' founders. Everyone involved in the company is about servant leadership.

It was not until after I decided to stay in Orlando that I realized Qivana's mission and vision were the same as Malaysian Urban Retreat (Murfest), which I had worked with in Malaysia. Murfest is a Yoga, music, and dance festival—the first of its kind of this magnitude in South East Asia. The exciting part of this is that I am working on developing a collaboration to propel both of these amazing companies around South East Asia together.

Qivana is a paradigm-shifting company with no intention other than the betterment of health, creating revenue for social good and financial empowerment. I am so grateful that I get to work directly with the founders. I love being involved in something with a vision so large, creating a grass roots, global movement of holistic health and scientific breakthroughs to spread worldwide. I was born to be a connector, and I have adopted two amazing new families along the way.

Only once I started putting my heart into Qivana did I realize what the car accident had given me. The settlement that I received had allowed me to explore the world and to find my own way.

Why was I given the chance to experience the horrific challenges and depth of darkness in my life? I now have all that experience to share with others, I would never be able to rise to such amazing strengths and connect at such depth if I hadn't gone through it all. The key to life is acceptance and living without fear in all of life's situations. Fear is the past and further, the present is our reality. Live in flow and without fear, without judgment. You can change your perspective of your situation; you can change your world and the world around you.

About the Author

Alysa Huppler-Poliak is originally from the interior of British Columbia, Canada, though she has now become a young global leader. For her, life is about giving back to create a world that is full of more care, love, and empowerment. She was born to be a leader, has overcome a lot in life, and is grateful that at twenty-six it has all come together. A connector by character and value-creating win-win situations is where she thrives.

http://www.meetalysa.com/

The Secret Wisdom
of the Inner Voice

Dr. John Demartini

What better way of creating a more fulfilling life than by mastering the art of tuning into your most inspired and ingenious self, your inner voice? This voice is your guide of all guides to a life of greatness. You cannot attune to this inspiring voice without living a more inspiring life. Genius, creativity, and a silent power emerge from your heart and mind the moment you do. The secret of tuning into its magnificent messages is having a heart filled with gratitude. When your heart is opened wide with gratitude, your inner voice becomes loud and clear, and your most life expanding messages enter into your mind with ease. If your heart is filled with gratitude, it is almost impossible to stop your inner voice from speaking clearly and profoundly. Many great spiritual revelations and mental attributes are suddenly birthed from within you when your voice on the inside becomes louder than the many voices or opinions on the outside. The immortal masters of life have been those who have mastered the ability to attune to their great inner voices. Those great beings that mastered this talent left their marks in history. From Christ, who listened to his heavenly Father, to Dante, who listened to Beatrice, to Walt Whitman and many others who listened to their guiding whisper, all have impacted humanity with the resultant immortal expressions of their inner voice. As your voice on the inside grows in clarity and strength so will your inspiration when you listen. Begin attuning to that inspiring station from within. Listen as it guides you to new levels of creativity and operation. Your inner voice will put few or no limits on your life. Only the many outer voices of others who allow themselves to live a life of mediocrity will do so. Decide now to expand your wisdom and fulfilment through such careful listening. Follow the steps below and commune with this wise inner guide. It will help you create a greater contribution to others and possibly even a legacy.

1. Stand relaxed with your hands loosely at your side. Take a few deep breaths. Inhale and exhale through the nose slowly.

2. Tilt your head up 30 degrees.

3. Turn your eyes up another 30 degrees, until you are looking forward and upward.

4. Close your eyelids and let them become relaxed.

5. Think about something or someone you are truly and deeply grateful for.

6. Keep thinking and thanking until you feel your heart has truly opened up and you have even experienced a tear of inspiration.

7. Upon attaining a grateful state, now ask your inner voice for any guiding message. Ask, "Inner voice do you have a message for me at this moment?"

8. When you are grateful enough and you ask for a message, a message will clearly come.

9. Write this message down.

10. If your message does not become immediately and clearly revealed, repeat steps 6 to 10 until it does.

When you are truly grateful, you will receive amazing and inspiring inner messages. These messages will be more powerful than might at first seem. The master, the genius, is the one who listens carefully. When you are grateful and your heart becomes opened, you will have revealed before your mind the inner message you would love to fulfill. These priceless gems of guiding revelation will assist you in living a life of greatness.

Be sure to act on your inspirations as soon as possible. When you don't follow the inspirations and intuitions of your inner voice promptly, you can begin to emotionally beat yourself up. This is not terrible though, for it is simply part of the grand and magnificent design of conscious evolution. It is a blessing for it assures that, no matter what happens, you will eventually learn and gradually or immediately unfold your inner spiritual mission, talent, and destiny. Life events will at times force you to listen to that wise voice within. The inspired beings throughout history learned to follow it. Those who have ignored it have passed by many opportunities it could have provided. For decades, many psychologists have considered individuals who have heard their inner voices as bordering on the edge of sanity. But, if you look carefully at the many great spiritual leaders, scientists, artists, musicians, and social leaders, they regularly listened to their inner voices. They gratefully awakened this special inner communion regularly. The great philosophers have stated that they would rather have the whole world against them than their own inner soul. Today, you have an opportunity for expanding your greatness. When your wise and masterful voice on the inside becomes greater than the many little voices on the outside, a life of great fulfilment, wisdom, and genius can become yours.

About the Author

Dr Demartini is considered one of the world's leading authorities on human behavior and personal development. He is the founder of the Demartini Institute, a private research and education organization with a curriculum of over seventy-two different courses covering multiple aspects of human development.

http://www.drdemartini.com

Your "Y"

Brandy Simison

It has been said that, if given a choice, people would rather die than experience cognitive dissonance. Now, I know this sounds a little dramatic, but it's true. The mental conflict that one experiences when their beliefs are contradicted by new information can be so overwhelming that people tend to reject it as being invalid, continue on with their lives without changing their beliefs, and ultimately die without ever really accepting the new information. But what happens when you are staring at undeniable, black-and-white evidence of new information—i.e. the truth? What happens when you find out the foundation on which you had built your life around was unsound all along?

Let me tell you, mental conflict was only part of my equation. My stomach felt as if it was in knots. It was hard to breathe. My head was spinning and pounding at the same time. I *literally* felt nauseous. I had discovered that the person I had spent the last eight years of my life with, the person I grew into adulthood with, the very same person I had envisioned spending the rest of my life with, had been unfaithful for years. Even with the irrefutable evidence, I started to reason that the proof could be false. But there it was, plain as day, and I had to accept it. I then just felt empty—like the life had been taken out of me. "Why?" I questioned. But the answer could only reveal itself in time. The eventual acceptance that it was no longer "us", that it was now just "me", brought on a whole new future. One I had only briefly envisioned.

I began to get really curious about who *I* was and what I wanted out of life. I started to question everything. It truly is something else to have a reality ripped away from out of you; it leaves you questioning the validity of all your beliefs. For if one belief could be false all along, so could another. I brought into question the fundamentals of who I was—or, rather, who I thought I was. I began bringing into question my sexuality. I knew I had always appreciated the feminine figure, and I had even briefly tested my feelings when I was sixteen, but I had never really given my feelings true consideration. So I began to be open to the idea that I may be attracted to women. I really opened myself up to all the possibilities, and there's a funny thing about being open to possibilities: opportunities begin to present themselves.

I met this amazing woman. She was gorgeous: tall, slender, and had these piercing, blue eyes. Moreover, she was upbeat; had a sense of humor; and, boy, was she talented! I swear my heart melted when she first sang to me with that guitar in her lap. And, what's more, she was totally in touch with her sexuality. It really is attractive to see someone who genuinely isn't afraid to express themselves. I learned a lot in my time with her. I came to the understanding that there is a spectrum to sexuality most comparable to the color spectrum. That sexuality cannot unequivocally be categorized into the classifications of gay, bi-sexual, and straight. You have the main colors—green, red, and blue (gay, straight, and transgender)— but you also have all the other colors that result: yellow, orange, pink, purple, violet, etc., each with their own amounts of green, red, and blue in them. I believe this is why, either knowingly or unknowingly, matters of gender identity are expressed with many colors. This understanding allowed to me to accept myself for the unique color I am.

I then began to develop a passion for life. Always being highly ambitious and now no longer having to plan for "us" allowed the luxury of dreaming without limits. I soon came to understand what my soul was yearning for: to see the world. But I also wanted to stay on track with my goals, so I began looking at higher-education overseas. And there it was. The University of Oxford offered a program that was absolutely perfect, so I went for it! I really opened myself up to the possibility that I could be «a student at the University of Oxford».

I will never forget the morning I received the email that I was called for an interview. I could hardly contain myself; I was completely and utterly elated.

During my travel to the interview, I was able to explore London. I saw the Buckingham Palace, all of downtown including Westminster Abbey, and even went up on the London Eye. That trip is still one of my fondest memories. But I have never been so completely and totally overjoyed as when I was notified of my acceptance. You better believe *all* of my family was called to share in that success! What's more is that, at this point, I was able to clearly see the "Y" as a symbol of the fork in my path to answer my earlier question of "Why?" Meaning, I could see that if I would have kept going down the path I was on, I would've ended up entirely committing myself to a man who was untrue to me, and I would not have allowed myself the process of self-discovery that led me to be the independent person I am today.

A few months later, I once again found myself asking, "Why?" I was at the UK border in London. I had just finished filling out my declaration card and was approaching the Border Force official. She had this stern look on her face as though she was a very serious, prim woman. I promptly handed her my declaration card and passport. "Where's your Visa?" she asked. I explained the details of my course and eventually showed her my offer letter that clearly identified me as a student visitor. I was then ushered to the holding area, which was directly in between two lines of people. So there I sat, weeping, while at least a hundred people went by.

After waiting hours in the holding area, I was ultimately fingerprinted; photographed; had my luggage completely searched; and finally, formally interviewed. After about eight hours of this whole detention process, I was released with my passport seized and issued a mandatory ticket home, only allowing me four days in the country. My program director worked tirelessly, composing a case to the UK Border Force asking for a pardon for myself and future course attendees, but to no avail. I was sent home, now completely and utterly disheartened—the antithesis of how I arrived. I took my case of clearly being misinformed all the way up to the vice chancellor of Oxford. The ultimate resolution being that since I could not prove I was *directly* misinformed, I was not entitled to much.

It truly is funny how life works. Usually, the blessings that come disguised as tragedies are the ones we end up being the most thankful for. After being redirected from Oxford, I kept yearning for mind expanding experiences with the intention of seeking answers to life's mysteries. I soon found that life can be a process of creation rather than discovery. I started applying my newly acquired knowledge, and once again really opened myself up to the world of possibilities.

I soon found myself growing in ways I didn't know possible. I transformed my tragedies into stories. I shifted from limited thinking to free thinking. I found myself continually developing my own model of growth and envisioning uplifting people to take open individuals from confusion to clarity, from unknowing to enlightenment, from obligatory action to inspired action. *I certainly found the "Y" in my "Why?"* It is my passionate purpose to empower people, and I am here now to do just that. Who knows whether I would've discovered my passionate purpose without my tragedies—but my guess is that I wouldn't have. Bless yourself and your tragedies, for they are unique times in your life when you are forming a new path—AKA, your "Y".

About the Author

Brandy Simison is a transformational life coach and psychiatric rehabilitation practitioner. Brandy is known for her unparalleled interpersonal skills and her unique culmination of evidence-based methodologies that allow her clients to not only accomplish (S.M.A.R.T.) goals, but re-imprint (neural plasticity) their past traumas so that they may arise into their full potential. This absolute G.R.O.W.T.H. program has earned her the reputation of being a powerful force in the field of personal development.

http://www.claritylifecoaching.org

Still Breathing

Llana Collie

Domestic violence: two words when spoken evoke such strong emotions. Two words when spoken, most people find them confronting, particularly when they are unaware about domestic violence and that it is happening around, or even to, them.

Domestic violence doesn't discriminate and has no boundaries, and affects people from all walks of life, regardless of gender, race, class, sexual orientation, age, or religious beliefs. It is the abuse of power and control.

It was late 2010, and I was feeling lost, like my life had no direction. I was a stay-at-home mum, and yet I was feeling empty, lost, and on an emotional roller coaster. I had fallen into an emotional black hole and doubted my abilities as a wife and mother.

Fast forward three years when a very dear friend of mine encouraged me to make a phone call to the domestic violence unit as she had identified the signs of my abuse.

I rang them without really understanding why I was calling. They made sure I was safe, and an appointment was made. I was a blubbering mess throughout the phone call. I was feeling overwhelmed, trying to process the emotions . . . and yet there was a quiet knowingness that there was something more.

After making the appointment, I broke down, not really comprehending whether or not I really needed to see them. A few days later, I called back and canceled the appointment. It was to take me another three months before accepting that I needed some help, guidance, and understanding of my situation. I called the domestic violence unit, made an appointment, and kept it.

The day arrived for my appointment. The domestic violence unit is a nondescript building for obvious reasons, and after being buzzed in I sat down in the foyer and started to sob quietly, not believing where I was. *Me* at the domestic violence unit! Never in my wildest dreams had I ever expected to be in a position where I would seek help for domestic violence. I found just being there quite confronting.

I spoke with a psychologist there, and she advised that I was, in fact, a victim of domestic violence. I was so unaware of domestic violence and the forms of abuse that fall into this category. This opened the floodgate of tears when the realization came that the reason for the emotional roller coaster I was on happened to be more than just the relationship problems we had been experiencing— that there was something bigger at play.

I felt like I had landed, someone understood me, heard me, and saw me. More importantly, it was reassuring for someone there to believe I wasn't crazy. That what I was experiencing was very real.

The gift in meeting with the domestic violence unit was that I gained an understanding of my situation. Once I had the awareness, I was able to step back and respond. With having awareness comes the ability to respond, as opposed to reacting.

I attribute three pivotal points in my journey of "surviving and thriving" after being in an abusive relationship.

The first was having an awareness of my situation, as it gave me the courage to seek more information and educate myself about the mindset of abusers. I found the knowledge I gained assisted partly in rebuilding my sense of self and that the abuse was more about the abuser than me. Yes, I had attracted the person into my life due to the emotional baggage I was carrying with me—and that was for me to own and deal with.

The second was unconditional support. Mine came in the form of professionals, such as a life coach, a psychologist, and a group of close friends and Facebook buddies. My support team provided me with a safe space to land when I needed it; and, trust me, at times I was raw after having been emotionally and psychologically battered for many years. My psychologist was able to support me through providing practical strategies to assist me deal with my partner. My life coach assisted me to dig deeper, to uncover why I had attracted this person into my life, to deal/clear the emotional baggage surrounding past experiences, and to reaffirm that I am OK and enough. My friends were there to lend an ear and provide a hug when I needed it.

The third pivotal point was probably the most difficult to achieve. I moved out of the family home on my third attempt. Yes, it took me two prior attempts to call the relationship quits, as they use your emotional vulnerability against you and make you feel guilty, then you end up staying.

Leaving is by far the most difficult thing to do. Not only are you emotionally vulnerable, but you also face other considerations, such as how to survive financially. Also, what about the children—and how will they cope? What will the co-parenting schedule look like? Will he have the children taken off me? Yes, some of my fears were irrational, but at the same time very real for me due to the mental and emotional space my head was in.

Moving out to a place of my own gave me the emotional space I needed to heal, to start trusting myself again, and to manage the abusive behavior directed at me.

It was through my increased awareness, continued unconditional support, and now distance that I was able to see the patterns of abusive behavior. I was able to start asserting myself, managing my emotions, and responding appropriately—rather than reacting, as I had done in the past.

It has now been eleven months since moving out and taking responsibility for my life.

A job literally fell on my lap two months ago, and I am ever so grateful that my employers, knowing some of the challenges I continued to face, were prepared to take me on.

For seven years, I have been out of the industry I was qualified in, still in a transition phase of my life as property settlement had only just occurred, and I was attempting to work out which way was up and where I was headed.

Interestingly enough, with re-entering the workforce I have been confronted with behaviors and situations that I believed I could handle and deal with. This was a huge kicker for me as what I was being shown was totally the opposite of what I believed I could handle. I was seeing similar behaviors in my work colleagues that I then found confronting and that threw me into an emotional spin.

I managed to juggle work, children, and life-balance for about six weeks before I lost the plot and broke down. It was my employer telling me not to be too hard on myself and that it will take time to get back on track and continue breathing.

Having this experience with work gave me the awareness and reaffirmed that life and recovery after abuse is a journey. There isn't a set time to draw a line in the sand and say "I am healed!" Healing is a journey and a process. I am grateful that I continue to have an amazing support crew to pick me up when I need it.

I am grateful that I am still breathing, as it means I have a new opportunity every moment to choose who I am and an opportunity for growth, healing, and moving forward.

Trust yourself; you are stronger than you realize. I urge you to seek assistance if you ever do find yourself in an abusive situation. If you are unsure where to go, start with your local doctor.

About the Author

Llana Colie continues to breathe by nurturing herself through being loving, compassionate, kind, and gentle first and foremost. She then is the best mum to her two children and a better person than she was the day before. She has commenced her studies to regain her financial planning qualifications and is also working on a project to inspire life-action through coaching others.

http://www.llanacollie.com

My Transformational Journey

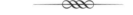

Dr. Francis H. Vala

What is about to be shared with you is a tragic reality that breaks my heart every time I remember it. I lost my best friend at age eighteen during the Iran-Iraq War. During times of military offensive strike, it was routine to use voluntary human forces to strategically clear minefields. If the path from point A to B needed to be cleared, the volunteers would line up, and the first one would run until a mine exploded, then the next one, and so forth. Once the path was cleared by these so-called "martyrs", the rest of the fellow comrades would proceed to complete the mission. I was devastated to hear that my best friend, YN, was one of those volunteers killed in a routine like that.

This incident triggered a range of profound questions, such as why are we fighting each other? Why are we losing so many innocent lives on both sides? Why do we have wars in the first place? How can we prevent them?

As an inquisitive teenager, I wanted to see a positive change, and craved to make a difference in the world, but didn't know how. Listening to a calling within me, I first became a physician to help others. Upon entering medical school at age nineteen, I was preoccupied by those questions. Frustrated by the fact that there was nowhere to find convincing answers, I became depressed for a short period of time. I realized that the burden of these thoughts was too much to handle for my age, and decided to continue living a "normal" life like everyone else.

Why do I need to know the answers after all?

I enjoyed many years of training as a medical student while maintaining a balance of "study hard, play hard". However, as I got to know patients more closely, I became aware of the tremendous amount of pain people were enduring. I realized that these sufferings don't just belong to other people, and was disturbed to find out that some of my close relatives were suffering from "narcotic addiction". This was another turning point in my life that again triggered the turmoil of curiosity within me. Why do people have so much pain in their lives? Why do people behave the way they do? How can I make a difference in a more effective way?

What better way to help people than to do what I was already set to do: to become a doctor, cure illnesses, and make a difference in their lives? Upon graduation from medical school at age twenty-five, I immediately began serving in a rural area in Iran. While seeing more than 120 patients a day during peak seasons, and feeling good about it, something deep inside was urging me to go beyond that . . . and I soon realized that I *can* and *must* do more. I didn't exactly know what to do next, but one thing was clear: to follow my inner guidance.

The tragic loss of my beloved father, which was my third wake up call, changed the path of my life.

It was the summer of 2002. The phone rang in the middle of the night. It was about 4 a.m. This did not sound good. Phone calls in the middle of the night usually reminded me of bad news. It was my uncle. The tone of his voice made me uncomfortable.

"I don't have good news for you, Farsheed," he said (that is my Persian name). I had a feeling I already knew what he was about to say.

"What happened, Hamid? Is it Dad?"

"Your dad is in the hospital," he said. "He had a massive heart attack. I'll call you back in a few minutes." He couldn't talk anymore. I could tell from his voice that he was devastated and couldn't hold his tears any longer. And you can imagine how I was feeling. I was in total shock. I didn't even know for a second how to feel. My father had shown no signs of heart disease until then, and he was only sixty-two. This was entirely unexpected. I couldn't help but call my uncle back after a few minutes . . . which felt like decades!

"Hamid, tell me the truth; I'm prepared for it," I told him, not knowing whether to believe myself or not.

"Your dad never made it to the hospital," he said. "He passed away immediately after a massive heart attack. I wanted to give you some time to absorb it."

My father had died of a condition called "sudden death". I was devastated. I could not sleep, eat, or work. I could do nothing and, for a brief period, I couldn't continue living. He was my best friend, my role model, my hero.

How could this happen to me? He was only sixty-two. This is not fair! What could I have done to prevent this tragedy? How could we prevent or delay physical illnesses? Is it possible to help people live longer and healthier?

In the next seventy-two hours, I was on the plane back to my home country to attend my father's funeral. One night in that first week of the ceremony, I had a dream. I dreamt of a poem describing my father. I woke up the next morning and started writing it down word by word. Today, that poem, printed on my father's image, is hanging on my bedroom wall. Seldom in my life to this date, apart from that occasion, have I been able to write a poem. In fact, my poetic talent is next to zero. I can hardly memorize more than two lines of a poem; so how on Earth did that happen?

It made me wonder! Obviously, it is a testimony that this poem was created somewhere in the depth of my brain, mind, soul, or somewhere in this universe. And, somehow, I had access to it. I realized that in certain deep emotional and mental states, the gate to a very mysterious, precious, and unlimited resource deep within our psyche opens up. Creative talents and capabilities surface to the world of reality like a volcano erupting from the center of Earth. This is called transcendence.

On my trip back to Canada, I vowed to pursue the search for the many profound questions that have haunted me throughout life.

Why do we have so many illnesses at individual, social, and global levels despite all the advancements in science and technology, and with thousands of leaders in the past or present? How can we prevent those illnesses?

The modern human being has lived on this planet for two hundred thousand years, and we experienced a major leap in civilization about six to seven thousand years ago. We have had enough time to figure those out. Yet, today, signs of global crisis—economic, political, cultural, and moral—warn us of a threat to the existence of humanity, as well as to thirty million other species belonging to this planet. The current civilization has failed to lead us humans to ultimate prosperity and happiness. The question is *why*? What are we collectively missing?

These daunting questions led to my journey trying to put together the pieces of the puzzle. I was determined to live my life in a more meaningful and purposeful way. After my father's sudden death in 2002, I finally realized my purpose was to write a book and contribute to global education and awareness. I started extensive research, accumulating evidence to some of the most unexplained concepts in humanity. The result of 10 years of research was my book *The Third Vision* published in 2013. I came to the same conclusion that Albert Einstein had reached: "We cannot solve the dilemmas of humanity with the same mind that created them!"

I realized that the common root of many illnesses, which humanity has been suffering from for thousands of years, is that the current vision we use to understand our self and the world is based on five limited senses. I refer to this as the "First and Second Vision".

For personal and global transformation to happen, we need a new vision—a new mentality and way of thinking to observe our internal and external world from a higher perspective than the one we're used to. That's what "The Third Vision" is all about, and it explains the most fundamental principles that apply to different aspects of life in a scientific and evidence-based approach, using a bio-psycho-socio-spiritual model.

It has been an amazing transformational journey in my life so far. Since the publication of my debut book, I have dedicated the rest of my life sharing my message and story with the world.

The message is simple: Human Empowerment And Transformation (H.E.A.T). Understanding who we are as humans, what we can be, and how we can make a significant impact in our life, as well as on the life of others, is crucial to determining the fate of humanity. As Rumi said 700 years ago, "I am not one drop in the ocean, but the entire ocean in one drop!"

About the Author

Francis H. Vala is a physician, public speaker, social entrepreneur, and clinical assistant professor at the University of British Columbia. Considering himself a "global citizen", he spent years studying the science of human development. Dreaming of a better world, he has dedicated the rest of his life to help *you* "Fulfill and Live Your Ultimate Potentials."

His vision: "I am not prepared to die without a contribution to the world!"

http://www.heatglobalcommunity.com
http://www.francisvala.com

Joy in Being Me

———— ∞ ————

Bonnie Wirth

This is actually quite an interesting place to be sitting, writing a story of healing and transformation. My healing journey has been quite significant; at the same time it is not yet complete. There is not just one area of my life that has been impacted more than another. There is not just one significant story of healing to share. The whole story is the entire journey, from unimaginable childhood trauma, depression, illness, and hopelessness to the unveiling and discovery of what I had been searching for the whole time: me.

You see, I know what it is like to feel hopeless and lost, to experience hardship, disappointment, and suffering. I understand what it feels like to be broken inside and to be in a state of deep despair. Yes, I have been there: where negative experiences cultivated and created even more negative ones. In fact, think of something and I have probably lived through it—or something very similar. But that's just some stuff that happened! More importantly, I took a chance on me, accepted the responsibility for my life, *every single part*, and moved forward one step at a time. As a result, I have brought about phenomenal transformation within my life. Self-responsibility is the most liberating act I know!

Let me take you back. . . .

Once upon a time, long, long ago in a city, town, or village not much different than your own, I had a bad-ass attitude within me. I was playing happy on the outside yet unhappy on the inside; caught up in the trauma, drama, and unforgiveness; and pretending to be unscathed while contemplating suicide and drinking too much wine. I was feeling hopeless, helpless, and completely lost. I had reached a point in my life where I was totally exhausted from having to play the roles of who everyone else expected and accepted me to be. The truth of the matter is that my world within was broken from abuse, violence, and neglect. My body had so amazingly carried the suppressed emotional baggage of my past and was in distress from my eating disorder. Pain-filled memories were interrupting my ability to forge a healthy relationship with my husband while grieving deeply for those I lost and a childhood that haunted my dreams at night.

Bonnie, the great pretender. I really should have won an academy award for my portrayal of having it altogether. You see, no one close to me knew of the suffering I had created within myself. I was successfully holding down a full-time, stress-filled job, raising three remarkable children, and—to anyone who knew me—I was a happy-go-lucky woman. Yet my greatest blessing came when I reached a point where I couldn't pretend anymore. I was on the verge of a nervous breakdown; I was bursting at the seams.

I remember that significant moment of surrender. The night I had cried out to God to either take me from this life or to help me make sense of it, asking for my life and everything that I had lived through to mean something. *God, use me for good.*

Since miracles are only ever dreamed about or prayed for, the idea of experiencing miracles or actually creating them for myself is something many people shrug off as "wishful thinking", immediately discrediting it and telling me it is impossible. Yes, there are a few of you who may even argue that all things are decided by fate, or that karma is just playing its hand, or that it is actually the will of God. I am not saying any of that is wrong; it is just that, for me, I understand and experience life in a new way because I have taken an active, creative conscious and a self-aware role in my life.

We often petition for miracles, praying for change in our life when something "bad" happens. Ever hear the old adage, "God helps those who help themselves"? Well, nothing can be closer to the truth. You see, for much of my life, I was caught up in wounds, memories, and feelings of disgust for myself, topped off with low self-esteem and unworthiness, and caught up in drama and negative

tional energy. What I became aware of was that I was the only person who could do anything about it.

I began working with the philosophies around the power of positive thinking, understanding how to utilize positive emotional energy for creating much needed change and how to apply the principles governed by the natural laws of the Universe. It was far out there, like nothing I had ever done before, and that excited me! It was like suddenly I had a secret genie inside. I got my thinking right! Wishes and dreams began to manifest, and I was feeling better and better about everything . . . except for my past.

I was ashamed and full of regrets, resentments, and unforgiveness. I rejected everything about me, and I was *still* suffering. You see, you can only move forward so far before the past demands to be put to rest. Since traditional counseling had never been something I felt drawn towards, I began working with alternative therapies, holistic counseling, and energy modalities to release the trauma and shock in my body and to renew my sense of self. I began healing limiting belief systems and paradigms that were holding me back and preventing me from truly living the life I had been praying for, and I began utilizing the basic principles of universal law to continue moving forward. My spirit was healing, and I was happy! For the first time in my whole life, I felt safe, worthy, and deserving of being loved.

From this place of new found happiness, my ego soothed; and the Divine part of me, my higher self, took over. I started to make choices and decisions based on the guidance of my heart (the yummy feelings *yes*, the yucky ones *no*). I still do the same today. Whether for myself or toward others, I consciously make a choice to pour love into every possible situation. It really is as easy as reacting in anger, choosing resentment, or responding in hurtful ways. Yes, even when I may not agree! I simply ask to be released from judgment and for Love and Light to fill my conversations. I ask that my words be an expression of love and that peace prevail. Then, no matter how things play out, I know that I was the very best of me through it all.

One of our greatest needs as human beings is to be loved and to feel that we are worthy and deserving of receiving love. We need to feel like we are important and that somebody truly cares about us, wants us, and accepts us unconditionally. Truth of the matter is, it all starts within us! We have to give love to ourselves first before anything else can flow or fall into place for us, including happiness.

I now understand that everything is a choice and that everything comes back to self-love. The Universe works in magnificent ways, and brings to us everything that we have created for ourselves, for our highest good, and our evolution as a Spirit.

Choosing to experience life from a place of love is about growing and nurturing kindness, compassion, and acceptance of yourself. You have to be willing to love yourself so much that you make choices based on what is best for you, regardless of the opinions of others. You have to love yourself so much that there remains no room for harsh judgments. You have to be willing to forgive and to have compassion and acceptance. You have to be willing to choose love, for love is the only thing that is real.

I know what is in my heart. It is love and it is just the same as yours. I believe that we all come from the same place and that we are *one* with the same, no matter the race, religion, culture, nationality, or creed. I choose to infuse love into all situations and into all my relationships because it is greater than any perceived differences. I believe that unconditional love is the greatest and the most generous gift to give. Opening my heart, and loving *me* wholly and completely, has influenced even greater unconditional love for others. Loving myself has helped me accept myself exactly how I am, *I mean exactly for who I am, the Me that God created Me to be.* There is now joy in being me.

So, my friends, next time you catch yourself thinking about what someone else is thinking about you, remind yourself that "It is none of your business." Focus on loving and accepting yourself for who you are. Miracles really do exist and maybe from this place of self-love consciousness, maybe . . . just maybe . . . you are the miracle you have been praying for too!

About the Author

Bonnie Wirth, a universal empowerment facilitator, is often referred to as the "Ultimate Soul Coach". She is an inspirational speaker, sought after self-empowerment consultant, co-facilitator of the "Experience Yourself" women's retreats, and editor-in-chief of PUREOne Magazine. Bonnie's passion for helping others comes as a result of her own personal life experiences, which inspire and support her commitment in raising consciousness while assisting people to initiate healing within and to embrace their life with authenticity, passion, and appreciation.

http://www.bonniewirth.net

How I Learned to Love
+ Be the *REAL* Me

Dr. Andrea Pennington

I n August of 2005, I asked God to take my life.

After an impromptu vocal performance in a dreamy night club in St. Tropez, France, exhilarated but confused, I was ready for my life to be over. No, I wasn't drunk or drugged up. I was so blissed out, temporarily living the life I *really* wanted, that I didn't know what to do with myself.

From the outside, it appeared that I had an ideal life. A beautiful home, sexy convertible car, million-dollar business, and plenty of money in the bank. Only three years into my professional career and I had already published my first book, appeared on *Oprah* multiple times, and was quite famous.

America's Empowerment Doctor. That's what I was known as, for setting people free from disease, depression, and dead-end careers. I appeared in magazines and TV talk-shows, flashing a bright smile from ear to ear.

On the inside, I was miserable, however. Nobody could tell, of course. I didn't like who I had become. My media image was that of a prudish know-it-all who wasn't following her own advice: "Honor your dreams; they are the treasures of your soul."

Yeah, right! I'm a performing artist with a medical degree—an actress who plays a doctor on TV. Yet, I wasn't honoring my dream to sing, act, and perform. Instead, I secretly lived with depression for over a decade.

My life felt like a lie, except for that glorious night in the south of France. During my artist retreat vacation, I courageously sang my heart out to a club of partygoers who didn't know my name, and it was pure bliss! A far cry from the boring routine I lived back in the US. The very dim life I was set to return to in a matter of days.

Following the ecstasy of entertaining, I returned to my hotel room. All alone, the familiar dark mood returned, and I cried out to God to take it all: my body, talents, and business. I said, "I don't know what I'm doing with my life! *You* take it!"

I was wracked with an intense longing for meaning, a glimmer of joy, some kind of relief. I wasn't suicidal. I would not have harmed myself. But I wanted out of my personal pain. In total despair, I sobbed and doubled over as my body trembled intensely. What happened next, which I've shared extensively elsewhere, was a mystical, out-of-body, near-death-like experience, where I thought God was answering my prayer.

Peace overtook me, and I felt as though I melted into the bed. I no longer felt like "me". I was aware of the concept of *Andrea Pennington*, but I felt I was *more* than her. I felt complete *Oneness* and absolute, pure love: for myself and all of existence!

From a detached perspective, I could see an overview of my life. I understood how my choices led me to the depressive state I lived in, and several important lessons came to me that totally set me free.

First, from that expanded state of awareness, I realized that pure consciousness inhabits all living things on Earth. I *am* one with that consciousness.

Second, though I am one with all consciousness, I do have my own particular essence: a soul. My soul has particular tendencies and preferences, which I now call the "Soulprint". As a human, I become what *I* choose, consciously or unconsciously. The earthly expression of my soul essence is totally of my choosing, and there is no "wrongness" in my choice. There is no God judging me, but my actions bear fruit and consequences.

Third, as I am an offshoot of pure consciousness, I am totally loveable, perfect, and complete.

I realized that my whole life had been leading me to one major realization, something that our souls know all along: in order to enjoy a life of total wellness and happiness, we must become who we really are—not who parents, society, or religion force us to be. To do this, we must *learn, live, and love* who we *really* are.

A flow of messages came to me, and I was filled with a quiet, joyful sense of wellbeing. Here they are:

> *It is normal to want to be seen for who we are; that's why we came here. We all want to be embraced and cherished for who we really are; that's our birthright. We all want to express ourselves wholeheartedly and to share ourselves meaningfully with others; that's our soul's greatest desire.*
>
> *True happiness comes from within, and it comes naturally when we integrate our whole being. We all want to have an impact in the world, to feel fulfilled knowing that we make a difference because, deep down in our soul, we know that we do matter.*

As I allowed the peace to bypass and replace all of my previous thinking and biases, I felt a total acceptance to return to my life but with renewed enthusiasm to live according to my soul's deepest desires. I said *yes* to life, and a few days later I returned to America a changed woman.

Curious and hungry to understand what I had experienced, I gradually withdrew from the media limelight to heal and to get to know the real me. I plunged into research of near-death experiences, studied the neuropsychology of consciousness, and read classic works by early mystics. I met shamans, a curandera, and meditation masters.

As I explored my family of origin, it was easy to see how I'd been programmed into conformity and taught to distrust my own heart. My father's insistence that a career in the arts wasn't reliable and his advice to pursue higher education drove my artistic passion into hiding. Every time I wanted to sing or create for art's sake, I felt self-loathing well up within me! I was driven to achieve academically and professionally to the detriment of my dreams.

Of course, my story is not unique. We have all been conditioned to live inside a predefined set of rules and expectations and forced to live inside a box. The programming of our self-image begins in childhood. From birth, the immature ego is formed and struggles to manage our behaviors, balancing desire for self-expression while seeking approval and acceptance of others. Through the socialization process, we adopt the beliefs of others that can cause our own self-rejection and self-loathing.

Though I had a gut instinct that my purpose lay somewhere outside the box, I felt trapped, afraid to break away from the seemingly "safe" life I had constructed. I resisted my innate tendencies and ended up masquerading as a half-baked version of myself, driving unacceptable parts of my personality into the shadows. The artist in me, when allowed to play and perform, allows me to enter the flow state where I feel blissfully whole and perfect—just as I am. Yet my programming plummeted me into self-rejection, shame, and sadness when strong urges of creative self-expression overtook me.

For years, I struggled against being and expressing my true nature and interests. I compensated with more achievement and education. In retrospect, looking over my medical career, I see how some of my patients' lack of self-love led them to similarly sabotage their addiction recovery or weight loss efforts.

Can you relate to this in any way?

I have since learned that by not engaging and expressing our true potential, we become hopeless and miserable. We may be functional, but not fulfilled; successful, but not satisfied. Limited by low self-confidence, we use life circumstances to justify our inaction when it is really our own fear of rejection, judgment, failure, or fear of success. We compromise reaching for our dreams and find it easier to surrender to pre-defined roles and expectations.

But there comes a time when we must say, "Enough is enough!" The desire to break free and live a new way becomes stronger than our fear. The soul stirs us into action where our strengths can be used to revive the true self, rewrite the self-description, recreate the self-image, and rebuild the living temple of our authentic self.

After cutting the ties with my former way of life, I began an intensive meditation, Yoga and Qigong practice. Through deep introspection and living from my strengths and desires, I now feel confident in who I am. Anchored in my truth, I have consciously constructed my life and career on my own terms. Now, I truly love myself and enjoy greater wellbeing than I thought possible!

My path was quite a convoluted adventure to total wellness and personal fulfillment. I don't think you need to perform onstage or have an out-of-body, near-death experience to learn—or remember—that you are totally loveable as you are. I hope my story shows that when our true nature is allowed to flourish, innovation and creativity outweigh the tendency toward conformity and competition. Peace, joy, and inner harmony can naturally outweigh frustration, depression, and addiction.

My passion is to empower others to live authentically with purpose and passion by discovering your unique Soulprint and becoming who you *really* are. I believe this is the way to consciously create a life filled with meaning, power, and fulfillment. This is how you will have an extraordinary impact in the world.

And the world really does need your authentic, original expression. We are part of an interconnected living organism, and what you do individually matters to us collectively. Your personality, character, values, and talents are all unique, and they are essential to the health and wellbeing of both you and the whole of humanity. You are a gift to the world!

About the Author

Dr. Andrea Pennington is a respected mind-body medicine physician, acupuncturist, and leading authority on wellness and transformation. She blends personalized medicine with positive psychology to empower people to go from "surviving" to "thriving" by embracing their talents and strengths to transform their life and business in honor of their dreams. A sought-after TV personality with multiple appearances on *Oprah* and *Dr. Oz.*, she provides media strategy consulting and personal brand mentorship around the world.

http://www.andreapennington.com

From Darkness to Light

Heidi Clifton

Always different. I was the black sheep. I used to look at the kids in school confusedly, like I was from another planet. The way they behaved was foreign to me. Why was everyone so horrible to one another?

High school was the same. I observed and kept to myself. I wanted to be part of it at times, to be a cool person, but I wouldn't change. I could see through the façade that was coolness, and I was far from it. So I kept my close friends close and watched from the sidelines. Midway through high school, I realized that, although I was being true to myself, I was bordering on being antisocial. So when I left school, I decided to be a hairdresser, forcing myself to be sociable. It felt right deep down inside.

I finished school and entered the hairdressing world. I struggled at first, not with the craft, but with the social aspect. I was the hairdresser who listened, but rarely spoke of myself. I now know that was why people began sending more people to me: because I listened, not just to their problems, but also to what they wanted. I gave them what they asked for, not what I felt like. I grew to love my job as it gave me the chance to create amazing things and to help people, especially with their self-esteem. After all, bad hair can shatter somebody's confidence in a second!

Over time, I challenged myself with my own business. I was twenty-four and felt challenged and empowered! I had the business four years, in which I learned so much. I also had a great relationship during this time. I was happy. At the time, life couldn't have been better. I loved my job, and my boyfriend adored me. I felt safe. In hindsight, something didn't feel right. Maybe I had fallen into "what is supposed to be" mode?

I had come out of my shell and was sharing amazing experiences with many people. Life ticked the boxes; however, toward the end of the four years, the cracks appeared. The business was consuming my life. My life was work. The first two years I had worked two jobs, and a lot of hours, but that was where I had met my boyfriend. We got to spend time together at and outside work. We had fun times. Once I gave that up and put everything into the business, things fell apart. I was never home. I had time for nothing but work. I knew it was time to let go of the business, and so, not long after, my relationship too.

Nearly thirty, a life swept clean. Although I knew it was necessary, I felt so lost and empty. I felt that pinch of society expectation. I cried endlessly, I had lost everything, and I felt like my heart had been ripped out and shredded. I was living at my parents out of boxes, working every hour possible to pay my debts and to distract myself from life. Easter gave me four days off work, but I had no idea what to do with the time. I ended up at the local oval in tears. I felt so isolated and empty. How can the right thing feel so wrong? Work had become my life, all I knew. Outside of that, I didn't know how to function. Instead of addressing this, I worked harder until the Universe bought me to a brutal stop.

I was heading out with Mum on my RDO when we had a major car accident. I was the passenger, and, as we crossed an intersection, a car came flying over the hill and straight into my door. Our car flipped in the air, rolled, and landed on its side. I looked out the windscreen. I was high side up. A guy was looking through the windscreen. "Are you OK?" he asked. I looked around. Adrenaline flowing. I tried the door, but it wouldn't open—it was caved in. I tried the sunroof, and it opened. A miracle! Mum was panicking. I had to get help.

As I stepped out the roof, a lady said to me, "There's broken glass and you have no shoes!" I replied, "There are bigger problems." And I collapsed. The pain kicked in—pure agony like nothing else. They filled me with morphine and took me to the hospital. I was X-rayed and was continuously given more morphine as they wanted me to walk. Eventually, I did and was discharged and driven home. That night, medication wore off and agony prevailed. My whole torso began convulsing. I screamed and cried, and every time I had to move, my parents helped me. In the shower, the toilet. The pain? Indescribable. The situation: degrading.

The next day I was told they had found fractures in my spine and that I was to keep movement minimal.

This was the beginning. . . .

Hairdressing was no longer an option, and this was confirmed by pain rehab six months later. All I knew had been taken away. I thought about what I could do, and I knew helping people was the answer. I studied counseling, which had my complete interest and kept me focused, giving me a purpose. It seemed commonsense and natural to me—so I knew I could do it, and do it well.

I had a lot of time on my hands, and I had to learn how to use it. To learn what life really was. This was my lesson. Brutal, but effective. 24/7 to occupy myself. It takes time, but you can master it; however, you must listen to yourself and the Universe! Lesson duly noted!

Six months into my recovery, I began a relationship with someone I had known for years who had returned to my life. For many reasons, however, it didn't work out. This time, I was on the edge. I was sliding. I wondered if anyone would ever want a broken person. With so many physical limitations, would I just be holding someone back? I really believed that I wasn't good enough and that I would be restricting anyone who was with me. Taking away their opportunities for fun and freedom. I thought maybe this was it and that I would be by myself forever and that's what was meant to be. The prospect pulled at my heart and crushed me. I felt like I didn't deserve anything good, like I was being punished. Maybe it was punishment for not fitting in? I was well and truly lost.

I found myself a house to move to. I needed to feel like I could manage myself. I needed to feel useful, and being back at my parents again wasn't going to help.

I began art classes, which were healing for me. It was freeing my creative side. But I was struggling to pay for it. I had help from friends as they could see the benefits for me. Art truly does heal, and it helps me a lot. It was my anchor as things got dark.

I constantly struggled. I had no money, and insurance had stopped supporting me. I wondered if I would ever work again. I spiraled out of control into deep depression. I couldn't leave my house, even my bedroom. The anxiety was taking over. I sat there one day, looking at all my pain medication. *Just one day without pain, please!* I considered for a moment freeing myself from the pain by taking what was there. I pleaded and begged, someone please help me. I was scared, lost, confused. Years were passing, and I was still in agony every day. I'd had enough. In that moment of desperation, something happened. I snapped back to reality. I looked at the medication.

What had just happened?

A month later, a friend who wanted me to visit her In Queensland called. She paid, telling me I needed this. I was petrified as it meant I had to leave the house. But I went.

Once there, I realized this was the intervention of something bigger. My desperation had been heard. I realized I was ten minutes away from where a dear friend of mine had passed away, so I went to the place where it had happened. It was bittersweet, beautiful, but I felt empty, knowing what had happened here.

I sat there for a while; I could feel him. When I went to leave, a van was parked next to our car. The driver yelled out, "Heidi! It's been years. How are you?" I replied, "I'm good, thanks." Then my friend said, "I think you have mistaken her for someone else." In that moment, I realized I didn't know this man. I told him that I had come to pay my respects to a friend I lost here. He smiled cheekily and said, "But isn't it a beautiful place?" And then he walked away. I got in the car and my friend said, "What just happened?"

In that moment, I knew. That was my dear friend. He had bought me here. My prayers for help answered.

I returned home a different person. I see everything differently. Always with me, guiding and supporting me, he visits my dreams often and is always around if I start to slide. He always told me I worked too much and didn't *live*. I now see he was right. Life is precious and could be over in a heartbeat. Every moment must count. All I had been through had led to this moment. Opening the door for me to share my experience with others and help them find that light switch in the dark. Helping people muster faith in the darkest places *is* my job. To find the miracle in everything. All we need for our journey is within, waiting to surface. All we dream of is ours, we just have to take action and *believe*.

About the Author

Heidi Clifton is a writer, artist, counselor/life motivator, and the owner of Spirit Inspired Art & Living.

After a challenging life, being different and seeing life differently, Heidi was involved in an accident that changed her life and led her to understand her uniqueness. She works with people from all walks of life, helping them navigate what seems like the impossible to find their light in the darkness—the light that burns within all.

http:// www.heidiclifton.com.au

Fill Your Cup

Rory Callaghan

*O*ne day my cup was empty. I'm not sure if you can relate to this, but as a twenty-five-year-old health professional with his dream job, I felt unhappy and disconnected. I had followed the path to success that others had taught me.

I realized that everything I had become was a result of my own choices. Whether they were conditioned, guided, or manipulated is irrelevant. I had chosen my path to wellness and was not where I needed to be.

My highest value was to help people, but I couldn't even help myself. I was an oxymoron, a health professional without his health. I knew there must be a better way.

I looked back to my youth for some clues as to how I ended up here. Unhappy. Disconnected. I was born in a developed country full of opportunity. I was lucky. My single mother taught me to have a hard work ethic; my father taught me compassion and empathy through his struggles with homelessness and alcoholism. Had these influences played a role? Perhaps my work ethic pushed me too far, or perhaps my empathy and compassion for others caused me to give at the expense of my own health.

My experience through youth shaped my map of reality. I was lucky enough to have traveled and seen the world. The blank canvas of my young mind could not stretch back to its original dimensions. It was ready to paint life's masterpiece. Was everything meant to be colorful, or was darkness and grey part of the masterpiece too?

Looking back, I felt like I had been conditioned to get educated, go to school and university, get another degree, find a job, build someone else's dream, work my way to the top, pay off my debts, and build a family.

I was halfway along that journey when things started to change. One day, I woke up, stepped out of the rat race to retirement, and saw a whole new world.

After so many years of becoming stuck, unhappy, and disconnected, I stopped and stepped back.

I was at a point where I was tired of being sick; I was sick of being tired.

I began to wonder, "What am I here to do?"

Did anyone else feel this way, or was it just me?

My driver for change started with a desperate need to feel better and normal again. I just wish I had been inspired to change my path earlier.

To find a solution to how I felt, I reached out to my networks of specialists, health professionals, and healers from all walks of life. I spent thousands of dollars trying to find a way to feel good again, but there was no change. I felt robbed and let down by the health and wellness profession. I wondered whether anyone else was paying for a service and following a plan with no result or lasting change.

It made me realize that if a "health professional" with a double degree, networks, connections, and all the available resources could not find a solution, then how could anyone else? I became concerned for the people I cared about most.

Where was I even meant to start on this path to wellness?

Was it my mind, my nutrition, or my physical body? Was it perhaps my misalignment, or lack of spiritual purpose? Or maybe it was my job, my lifestyle, or the people I surrounded myself with.

Perhaps it was all of the above.

What role had my birthright or genetic blueprint that my parents had given me played? Was I a victim of circumstance or could I change this feeling?

I just wanted to feel better again.

Everyone I spoke to had an answer from their own perspective, learnings, and teachings, but rarely would anyone consider the

174

opinions of others. All opinions seemed valid, rational, and logical, but who was right and who could connect the dots?

To me it seemed like a minefield of misinformation where I was kept in a state of dis-ease. It was a vicious cycle and I didn't feel any different.

I realized everyone had only one piece of the puzzle to my problem. Some had small pieces; others had bigger ones. While others were playing a completely different puzzle altogether. I started understanding that to see the complete picture, as weird as it may seem, I had to look up.

To understand how I could change things, I needed to feel humbled by what I did not know. It gave me perspective. How could people speak in absolutes in any area of science, when the Hubble telescope taught me that every star I saw is a universe or galaxy just like ours? Science seemed to be our best guess, but it was just a rationalization of what we consciously thought we knew as a collective group.

So what had changed? The same day seventy years ago for our grandparents was drastically different to today. We have changed the landscape of our environment significantly. We have seen an evolution of our conscious mind, granting us the thought processes to manipulate our environment, creating an industrial and technological revolution. As a species, we have seen a global population boom at the expense of our environment.

Perhaps the answer is self-evident.

We just need to adapt to our new environment or make it more conducive to our survival. If through our choices we can make it unsustainable for life, then surely we should work toward doing the opposite.

If we cannot change our environment, then we need to focus on ourselves. Find a way to fill our own cup daily.

Within our own cup, there are parts that we can and cannot control.

We can consciously control our mind, thoughts, food intake, movement, and our passion for work and life. We can control our beliefs, spirituality, and sense of purpose. And even partially control our immediate environment and the people we surround ourselves with.

Some things we cannot control and seem predetermined. At birth, we cannot consciously control the environment or country we are born into. We cannot control our genetic blueprint or the framework our parents give us.

When I realized what I could and couldn't control, I started focusing my energy on what I *could* control. I had to detach from the things beyond my control. This is when my path to wellness began. *As a result, at the age of twenty-six, my cup was full.*

For me, it started with my mindset. I stepped back and realized that what I was doing was not serving me. I was unhappy and disconnected, so I decided to change something. . . . I made a choice.

I discovered that the foundation of healing was based on what I was feeding my body and how it was absorbed. I realized that my immediate environment was not serving me well. I quit my "dream job" and started moving, surfing, and doing things I loved. I had time and energy to invest into myself, and I regained self-love and self-worth while re-discovering my purpose in the process. I surrounded myself with positive, open-minded, driven people. I was a product of the five people I spent the most time with. As a result, everything I started to do felt good.

Finally, I was happy, connected, and seemed to consistently attract good people into my life.

It was at this time that I felt ready to help fill the cups of others. My purpose became focused on helping the people closest to me—family and friends—to fill theirs daily. Then empowering them to help others and do the same. Together we could create a global impact through connection and collaboration. Why do we need to change our approach? The statistics do not lie. The burden of preventable disease is increasing in the developed world. Obesity, cancer, and depression are primary causes of death. Processed, packaged foods, uncontrolled growths, and our thoughts are killing us! The less developed world is dying from a lack of basic human rights. I realized we needed an ecological approach. I could not stand by while I knew this and saw it impacting the people I cared about the most.

To heal ourselves, we have to be in an environment that allows us to do so. We have to find ways to fill our own cup daily. To help others, we need to give them access to open source information, so they can make better choices. Find the open-minded, ecological problem solvers that are not afraid to share their ideas and thoughts. Stand on the shoulders of giants so we can make the complex seem simple.

In an ideal world this new health and wellness system would work toward people being happy and connected.

To do this, we need to consider the person and their environment! It needs to be evidence-based, but outcome-focused. Prevention is the best cure. Dis-ease would become a transient state. People would be informed and empowered to self-manage their own pathway and journey to wellness. They would make and have informed choices with support.

However, I am a realist. Things are not ecological. I would like to leave this world in a better place than when I arrived, but I am aware of the paradox of our time. We all seem to know what to do, but choose not to do it. If we keep choosing to do the same thing over and over, expecting a different result, then perhaps Darwin was right: dis-evolution.

Just Imagine if we could create an environment where our friends, family, and children could thrive, not just survive. *Thrival*.

So let's keep this simple. It starts with you. Where do *you* start on your path to wellness?

First, ask yourself – Am I HAPPY?

-   If not, why not?

Second, ask yourself – Am I CONNECTED?

-   With myself?

-   To the people around me?

-   To the world I live in?

-   To my purpose?

Every day we make choices based on the best information available to us. But, if like me, one day you wake up unhappy and disconnected, why not change something? Be inspired, not desperate. Be open to new information. Make a choice today.

About the Author

Rory Callaghan is a Holistic Health Care Professional.

http://www.fillyourcup.com.au

Reflection

Rebecca Grainger

I was sitting alone in Green Park on a red and white stripy deckchair overlooking the London skyline, surrounded by city workers who were enjoying their lunch as an escape from their cubicle. It was a lovely sunny day, and I should have been ecstatic; I had found an investor for my online business. It was a dream come true.

I looked every part the corporate, power-dressing city slicker—on the outside. But inside, I was a mess. My head was a black hole of confusion; I couldn't see clearly or think straight. In fact, I felt like I couldn't think at all. I was on the brink of a life-changing opportunity that I had wanted, dreamed about, and worked hard for—for four years.

And all I wanted to do was exit and find peace from the mayhem in my head. I couldn't cope. The reality was, my life was slipping through my fingers. I felt like I was falling apart.

Yet at twenty-two, life had been rosy. I was a successful personal trainer with great clients, bright ideas, and a burning desire to make a change. I saw a gap in the online market and developed an eight-week lifestyle program combining healthy eating and exercise for wellness. It was a slog: long hours and high risk (it was the beginning of the dot-com bubble), but I was passionate, naïve, and thought I could do it all. I was featured in national UK newspapers, wrote for an online magazine, and was a health and fitness columnist in the local Welsh newspaper. I owned a garden apartment in a trendy

Cardiff suburb and had great friends and a busy social life. I was besotted with my gorgeous puppy and was in love. I was happy.

Four years later, it was a different story. I was working long hours as a personal trainer, running my online program, and trying to secure investment to develop the business, which was challenging in the turmoil following the dot-com bust that had erupted in 2000. My boyfriend's business partner had died suddenly, and our relationship quickly disintegrated into a hole of infidelity and dishonesty.

After five years together, with only shreds of self-respect left and in an attempt to find sanity, I walked away; I was too young and ill-equipped to deal with this. And, to top it off, I had been diagnosed with depression.

So, at twenty-six, I headed to my hometown; but with divorced parents and no family home to find solace in, I ended up living in a rented room with just a suitcase of belongings. I had hit rock bottom.

As I sat desolate, crying on that deckchair, it was the first and only time I ever considered that perhaps I could find peace if I wasn't here. Depression is so lonely, so confusing, and so heavy. I had been prescribed anti-depressants, yet I felt worse than ever. Blackness engulfed my thoughts with no light at the end of the tunnel. I felt like someone was standing on my chest, and I couldn't breathe. Carrying that "D" label—one I didn't want to share—was a burden.

It was in that moment, I knew something had to change.

I needed to relieve my head of the pressure I was under and find a way out of the black hole. At that lowest point, I had two choices: stay in darkness or find the light.

I remembered two clients who had introduced me to spirituality and the power of thought. At the time, when life was good, I hadn't taken much notice of it, but something in me triggered that memory. I had been told you could ask your Guardian Angels and Spirit Guides for help. So I did. I imagined a bright white channel going from the core of the earth up through me to the sky and universe above. For weeks, I prayed and continued to ask for help, clarity, and guidance.

I stopped taking the anti-depressants, walked away from my business, and, with no income to afford rent, I moved in with my sister onto her couch.

After many false starts, lots of tears, heartache, and nights drowning my sorrows, I began to realize there was no point in looking back and living in the past, in wondering what went wrong, and in trying to, somehow, change the outcome. Blame, anger, guilt, and hate are such worthless, negative feelings and a waste of energy.

The benefit of rock bottom is you have no choice but to make major life changes. After months of intense self-work and healing, I had released the pieces in my life that were causing so much pain, confusion, and helplessness. My apartment had been sold, and I used the money to escape. For the following year, I travelled—and, for the first time, I felt free.

I was literally on the other side of the world, in Australia, living day to day in the present moment, and a new me emerged.

The Universe is a wonderful, and sometimes baffling, place. It was here, on my runaway trip, that I met James. I was twenty-seven and working in a bar—so different from the life I had left behind. Ironically, it turned out that we both lived in Cardiff but had never met despite having mutual friends. Funny how the universe works! We spent a year together living the dream by the beach, inspired and thriving. We daydreamed about the life we could lead, the family we could have, and the freedom of living on our own terms. I believe now our thoughts held so much passion that our intentions were formed.

I had first visited Australia when I was sixteen and instantly felt like I was home. I left with the strongest desire to live there one day. I visited Australia three other times in the following ten years, every time wishing that one day it would be my life. Though unaware back then, I had re-affirmed my intention and was waiting for that path to arise.

After my runaway trip, we returned to Cardiff, but the drastic change to our carefree life and the rawness of going back sadly led me and James to part ways. I was unemployed and snapped up the first job I was offered, and, just like that, my recruitment career began.

It was at this time I first read *The Secret* and actively started to put into practice the Law of Attraction. I would affirm every day what I wanted in my life. And, sure enough, I had peace, health, wealth, luxury holidays, a busy social life, and a new home—I even had my dog back! I was happy, enjoying the life I had created.

Apart from a deep yearning to be somewhere else.

The Universe was working her magic behind the scenes: I had joined a global recruitment company that would sponsor and relocate me to Australia just seven years later. And so it was, on a one-way ticket at thirty-four, I returned to Australia with a job and a heart mixed with fear, trepidation, and excitement for my new life. The Universe had followed through on my dream that had started eighteen years previously!

I loved my new life. I returned to where I had lived, got an apartment overlooking the beach, commuted on the ferry to Sydney, built a fabulous group of friends, and thrived.

The only thing missing in my new life was someone to share it with. So having successfully changed my life, I used the same philosophies to attract my soul mate. I put out to the Universe what I wanted my husband to be like by writing a list of qualities and by making space in my home for someone new. I had healed my heart and had learned many lessons. I set a very clear intention that I was ready and trusted that he would come into my life at the right time.

I truly believe what is meant for you will not pass you by.

Only nine months into my new Australian life, I changed jobs and returned to the UK for a three-week holiday. James and I had remained friends, and I contacted him to meet up, but he had changed his number four days earlier. However, he had heard I was back and tracked me down in a bar. We spent the next two weeks together and decided then he would move to Australia. I put his new number in my phone as "James My Husband" and it remains there today.

He moved over two months later, proposed a month after, and three months later we were married in the town we first met in. We now have a beautiful son, and we walk along the beach we once did, now living the life we used to daydream about. I have since found out that James always believed we would be together, but just never knew how it would happen!

Trust that you can manifest your dreams.

I am so grateful for the journey my life has taken me on. I appreciate the present moment, and I'm grateful every day, finding something positive in the smallest of things. Our darkest moments can be our greatest teacher, so learn what you need to learn, and don't be afraid of change; it is not failure, it is growing.

Without that first step, you can never start your journey to realizing your dream.

About the Author

Rebecca Grainger is a career mentor, holistic coach, writer, and the founder of the "Edit Hub", which supports independent, overworked soul-seekers to create a life of balance, fulfillment, and happiness.

Combining over ten years of international recruitment experience with her personal healing journey, she believes in practicing what she preaches. She is on a mission to empower women to follow their dreams and to inspire them to take action and live a life where they thrive.

http://www.rebeccagrainger.com

Dedication, Determination, and Discipline of a Soul

Dr. Andrea D. Sullivan

When I was five years old, my oldest and dearest friend asked me what I wanted to be when I grew up. Immediately, I told her, "I want to save the world." She patted me on the head and said, "That's very nice." She was amused. I was serious.

I didn't know what that meant, but I knew I was here to do something that assisted others in being all that they could be; something that allowed others to shine and bring their talents to the planet; something that would bring healing and light to the darkness—not that my world was dark. Mine is not a story of familial abuse or neglect. While I did have an experience of sexual molestation that affected my self-esteem, I was fortunate in comparison to the stories I hear as a physician. I remember wanting to be a paleontologist, anthropologist, and then veterinarian, but somewhere that got lost as I saw Americans in pain from the disease of racism.

I went to a predominately Caucasian elementary school. It was a magical place. There was so much freedom, respect, and kindness. We celebrated and learned about each other's cultures and history. In junior high school my first boyfriend was Caucasian. He was kind, smart, and quiet. His thirst for knowledge attracted and inspired me. I began to feel the tentacles of racism then when he told me he couldn't like me because of his parents—because I was

African American. But it was not until my high-school experience that I was engulfed in its effects.

I understood that African Americans had a special history in this country. My mother's entire family was educated and descendants of a slave master in England. I could not trace my father's family beyond my great grandmother who was a slave, dark in complexion and uneducated. The dichotomies in my family between the house and field Negroes—as they were called—were obvious and significant. But what they had in common was dedication, determination, and discipline. Though my father was not formally educated, my parents knew the value of education. Given that I was a straight-A student from elementary to junior high school, my parents agreed I should go to the best academic high school in the city, especially because I didn't have to be tested. I was admitted based on my scholarship.

It was a predominantly white all-girls high school. I was continually being called to the Principal's office for some bogus event, like having permission to go to the bathroom and then being told I really didn't have any. Hiding in the basement of friends' homes while their parents entertained was customary. I didn't understand then what those events were doing to my self-esteem.

In my sophomore year, whatever strength and dignity remained was vanquished, when my counselor said, "You should not think about college. You should be a domestic worker." I stopped breathing for what seemed like an eternity, and I couldn't hear anymore. I only watched her lips move. My grandmother was a domestic worker and her mother a slave. Had my reading, learning, and studying not advanced me beyond their station in life? What would I tell my parents, friends, relatives when it was time to go to college? Words like embarrassment, shame, anguish, and despair don't and can't describe what I felt that day.

I never spoke a word of this until after I received my PhD in 1976. A reporter for a local newspaper asked to do a story about the one thing for which I thanked my parents most. My response was clear: going to college. When my parents asked me where I wanted to go to college, I told them I was going to secretarial school. My father said, "Oh, do I need to remind you that the only D you ever received was in typing?" After much conversation and rebuttal, I consented to go to college.

My first year was a miserable experience. Not just because I was away from home, but also because the school was old and the conditions were, at times, sub-standard. I ate a tuna cheeseburger and a pack of Twinkies, and followed that with a Mountain Dew almost every evening after dinner. I was determined to transfer and stay in school because I loved learning and the process of education. And transfer I did, albeit thirty pounds heavier. By December, I was enrolling in another university, subsequently graduated second in my class (only because I was a transfer student), and entered graduate school specifically to earn a Master's in sociology and criminology. My undergraduate experience came at a time when Dr. Martin Luther King Jr. and Senator Bobby Kennedy were assassinated. Attending all African American universities provided a different perspective than what I was used to: a rather reversed racism. But I wasn't accepting of that perspective either.

In graduate school, the dis-ease of racism was ever present in the classrooms, as professors would tell us the brains of black people were smaller and that this is why we committed more crime, or that black people *couldn't* learn and, thus, crime was the only avenue for our lives—imprisonment the only consequence. So often I wanted to run out of the classroom and never return. As the only African American in the entire department, it seemed as if time had stopped again, and breathing was shallow if at all, as the entire class looked at me to note my response. I was reliving high school and the words of my counselor.

I was studying one day and began to cry. I sobbed for an understanding of the hatred and atrocities in the world and for the inferiority and shame I felt to be both African American and female. Somehow, even though I was getting a PhD, I wasn't enough. It wasn't enough. I needed answers that were not of a physical world.

Though raised Episcopalian, I wasn't impressed because we prayed to a white Jesus and a God who lived in Heaven. I just did not believe that Jesus could be a white man, given the descriptions in the Bible and because of where he lived. I didn't believe God could be a white man because I looked nothing like that, and I was supposed to be made in His image. I was confused.

I sought answers. My searching led me to a spiritual group in California. They spoke of things like how we are all part of God and God is in each of us. The Kingdom of Heaven is within and seek ye first the Kingdom of Heaven and all else will be added unto you. Acceptance, forgiveness (of self for judging others), and loving always in all ways were teachings in seminars I attended.

I felt comfort and some understanding of this world as I heard that we are spirits in human form. We have come here to have a physical world experience and to complete the karma from another lifetime. We have come here for spiritual evolution—to know darkness in order to know light in a greater way. We are here to love one another.

With PhD in hand and some spiritual knowledge, I set out "to save the world", at least in the criminal justice system. I was delusional, as that system had already planned to be the end of a pipeline for the underserved and for the people of color. It did not take long for me to see I could not make an impact. Ultimately, I was asked to be a special assistant in a presidential administration.

While in that position I sought the advice of a naturopathic physician for my weight. I told him about my life, my shame from my high-school experience, and my evolution. He said, "You should be a naturopath." Go back to school for another four years? No way! I realized God had a different plan for my life when I found myself going back to a university where I had been an assistant professor, to take pre-requisites for naturopathic medical school.

I was the only African American in the school. I cried every day the first year for I had left everything I ever knew as love and home. People asked me if they could touch my hair or if we could be friends because they didn't know any black people. Thank God for my teachings. I was gracious and relentless in my pursuit of saving the world.

Between my second and third year, I took a break and studied with my spiritual group. I learned that *everyone* at some time feels inferior, that abuse was universal and not just in the black community, that we have so much pain it is difficult to see clearly who we really are: children of God, one people, one race—human. At the end of that year, I didn't just believe in God—I knew God. I knew God was in everything, everywhere, all the time.

My patients have affirmed what I know to be true. In 1998, my first book, *A Path To Healing: A Guide to Wellness For Body, Mind, and Soul*, was published. I wrote about the institution of slavery and how it created the worst dis-ease in America, about racism, and about how we can heal those wounds through naturopathic medicine. It speaks of all I have mentioned here and how we must make choices that support loving ourselves so that we can love others.

Daily, I am living my dream of saving the world, one soul at a time. I'm grateful for my dedication to humankind, my determination to let my light shine on the planet when I felt like hiding it, and my discipline to be obedient and faithful to the spirit.

About the Author

Dr. Andrea D. Sullivan received an ND (Doctor of Naturopathic Medicine) degree from Bastyr University in Seattle, Washington, in 1986, with a specialty in homeopathy. She has a private practice in Washington DC. In 1976, Dr. Sullivan received a PhD from the University of Pennsylvania in sociology/criminology.

Her books include *A Path To Healing: A Guide To Wellness For Body, Mind, and Soul* and *Enough! When Sacrifice Has Gone Too Far.*

http://www.drandreasullivan.com

Finding My Groove

Kim Adams

For years, I believed I was in control.

I am financially independent with a successful career, three children who were making their own way in the world, and a body that belies my forty-plus years. I pride myself on maintaining my petite figure that really hasn't changed much since my early twenties. I have postgraduate qualifications in psychology and management, a life-long Yoga and meditation practice, and a long interest in health, nutrition, fitness, and spirituality that has always been my support through difficult times.

To all outward appearances, I was the confident, funny extrovert who usually got what she wanted through determination and hard work. But at some point in 2012, this started to fall apart.

About fifteen years prior, a huge change happened in my life—change that I created and wanted, but that was to have a significant turning point in my life. I moved interstate to a city where I knew no-one to work in a totally new profession, while commencing postgraduate study, and to just raise the pressure. It was at this time I decided to end my eleven-year marriage to the father of my three children, who were all in primary school.

Two children remained with me while the middle son moved interstate with his father (cue disdainful looks from other women). So new city, new job, newly single mother, no car, studies, a mortgage, and barely getting from one paycheck to another.

So I put on my best fake-it-until-you-make-it smile and asked no-one for help. Hell no-one could know I needed help. That would be failure.

I took control of everything.

I became intensely involved in the fitness lifestyle and developed what I now see as seriously disordered eating patterns and exercising routines. I even counted the almonds I allowed myself for morning tea, and heaven forbid that fat or carbs would pass my lips. My life was consumed by a singular obsession with controlling food and my weight. Any digression from my "allowed food" or punishing exercise regime would result in feelings of shame, disgust, and panic.

On the up-side, I looked fantastic! I felt empowered! This internal and external illusion of success was fueled by the admiration, compliments, and approval of my peers . . . especially men.

My disordered eating and exercise was my survival mechanism allowing me to cope and feel in control. By taking control, I stayed sane. My tendency toward obsessive dieting, which had bubbled away underneath the surface for years, was my savior. My tightly scheduled exercise regime during a time of significant change and emotional stress was my security.

Fast-forward about twelve years and I was now back in my beloved Queensland in a management position that I loved, in an organization that I believed I would be in for a very long time. I had also just entered into a relationship with a wonderful man who was to clearly become my life partner and my rock, when the carefully constructed protective mechanisms I had developed began to fail me.

My job changed, the ethos and management changed, and suddenly I felt like a square peg in a round hole. The values I had around work disappeared, the simple act of walking into my office left me drained, and, for the first time in my life, I started to experience panic attacks in response to the simplest of matters. I had brain fog, my performance was failing, and I started being belligerent and difficult with colleagues. The darkness of depression was threatening to take control, and my GP diagnosed me with moderate to severe depression. Oh, how embarrassing. . . . No-one must find out!

On top of that, my ability to maintain my strict diet was wavering; I didn't want to exercise but was terrified of "getting fat".

My digestion was ruined from years of restrictive nutrition, resulting in almost constant constipation, bloating, and increasing sensitivity to more and more foods. It seemed like everything irritated my digestion. Hell, *everything* irritated me!

As my carefully constructed world was falling apart, that annoying voice that had been calling me for years was becoming more insistent. . . . I wanted to teach, I wanted to stand in front of groups of people and speak, I wanted to be heard. They say that to identify what your passion is, you should look at what came naturally to you as a child. My mother recalls that as a pre-schooler I would line up all the dogs, my cat, and my stuffed animals, and lecture to them long and loud.

But what was I to teach?

A confluence of events led me to believe that teaching English to Balinese youth might be my calling—and, at the very least, would be an escape from an intolerable situation at work. I had been to Ubud in Bali four times previously, and I felt a deep spiritual connection with the land and people. So I took nine-weeks leave to live and teach in Ubud.

Among the rice fields and solitude, while journaling and teaching English on the floor of a hut, I learned several things: I distinctly dislike the English language, and I let present perfect continuous verbs never be spoken of again; I love teaching; my passion is health; and I have a unique perspective that blends scientific training with my personal passions of mind-body-spirit coming from Eastern philosophies of health.

I also realized that much of what I had achieved was done in an effort to prove my worth to others and in a strange way to myself. My academic success, my financial and emotional independence, my perfectly maintained body . . . all of it was because I felt I wasn't perfect. So while I yearned to stand up and speak, deep down I believed that no-one would listen.

My constant control was not serving me anymore. It was holding me back from the real me, from the calling that I had to speak up and be heard.

My world was being turned upside down because Spirit was calling me to go deeper.

If I was to do that, I had to be vulnerable and to expose the real authentic Kim. Holy shit! Now, I was not comfortable with that realization at all!

My emotional and digestive health and my soul's purpose were demanding attention, and I returned from Bali with the seeds of my next stage of growth and a new vision for the future.

I then started to see women all around me who were just like me. Women who are smart and informed about health, but who were frustrated and simply tired of being told to eat less and exercise more to stay looking skinny, young, and pretty because that is what the media has us believe is worthy of value. Women who were struggling with digestive disorders that were not relieved through dietary restriction or medication; women who struggled silently with body image or never feeling quite good enough; women who didn't necessarily fit a medical diagnosis of having an eating disorder, but who suffered from disordered eating brought about by toxic nutritional beliefs of what health, beauty, and desirable meant.

This is the average woman who is tired of constantly battling food and her body.

I undertook specialist training through the Institute of Eating Psychology, and I am discovering a gentler, more nourishing relationship with food and my body. And *this* is what I am meant to be standing up and talking about.

So where am I now with my relationship with my body?

There was no single a-ha moment, no meditative state of bliss when I was delivered an angelic message of salvation. Believe me, I was looking for a clear message to be delivered by angels (or a unicorn would have been cool). But what I have come to realize is that such clarity would not have served me or those that I will serve. My own journey to wellness was meant to be a series of moments, of gentle shifts, and for most people I believe transformation is like that.

My digestion is about 80 percent good, and that's good enough because it is my early warning barometer that lets me know when something needs to be addressed. Am I holding onto anger? Am I taking on too much?

My relationship with food is a reflection of my relationship with life.

Do I still have dark days where I imagine I am about to spiral into fatness? Yes I do. But I now recognize the voice of my inner demons, trusting my authentic voice more than them. And if I can't manage to trust me, I am learning to trust my gorgeous guy, his love for me, and my body just the way it is.

Health isn't about eating perfectly, meditating perfectly, or nailing a Yoga headstand. Health is about listening to your inner truth, trusting in your body's messages, and taking actions that resonate with who you are. And, sometimes, health means having one too many margaritas and doing bad salsa to Ricky Martin.

So here I am, at forty-seven, living more in my own skin than ever before. Opening to trust and vulnerability, because I feel the strength in this and know deep down that there is really no alternative. I have to speak up and speak out from my heart, not just from my head. And the magic is that every single lesson, hurdle, or piece of knowledge that I've collected on my eclectic path through life actually all links beautifully together.

I am ready to be heard.

About the Author

Kim is a nutritional psychology coach, workshop and retreat facilitator, and Yoga teacher who connects women with their internal body wisdom so they can live life with passion and purpose. Kim blends psychology with mind-body-spirit philosophies, a straight-shooting approach, intuition, and a wicked sense of humor to inspire you to be in your optimum state of health.

http://www.happyhealthygroovy.com.au

Peace

Melanie Commons

Quiet. I do love stillness and quiet. That space in between movement and noise. This is my life now. A state of presence and an awareness of stillness and peace. My life hasn't always been this way. In fact my life was, for many years, in stark contrast to what it is today.

Let me take you back a few years.

Battersea, London. It was a cold and rainy day in May 2009, and I had been here for a few months after about half a year traveling through South America. I moved to London to get some clarity on what it was that I wanted from my life. Before London, I had been living in Sydney for nine years and I had left longing for change, inspiration, joy, and peace. My vision for London was to get a job in advertising and to travel through Europe—to settle and to ground myself.

My friend Thomas and I had been talking on the phone. He was back in Sydney and was asking about my next step. Without hesitation, or even careful thought for that matter, I declared, "I'm moving home, to the Gold Coast, and I want to become a Yoga teacher, live on the beach, and get a cat!"

Whoa! What? Where did that come from? I had just moved all of my life to London to begin again, and here I was claiming I was moving back to the Gold Coast!

I didn't realize it at the time, but that statement was the beginning of a wonderful healing journey. See, I have always had a strong intuition, and I have always felt the guidance of a force greater than me. I knew this was something that I was meant to do. It felt right.

The next day I set a date to leave Europe, I would travel around for a few more months and move back to my hometown and begin a new chapter of my life.

After moving home, to the Gold Coast, I spent my time working and doing Yoga and reconnecting with my family and friends who I had not seen for some time. A friend and I were chatting one day about Yoga training, and I decided I was going to take the plunge! I immersed myself in the teachings, philosophy, and history of it and loved the way it made me feel. I couldn't wait to share this with other people. What a gift! I felt so much gratitude to have this opportunity to spend time on myself. Learning this sacred, ancient way of living was so fulfilling!

Having my own business and running my own studio was one of my intentions that I had set while doing my training; this guidance came from within, from that little voice that I trusted had taken me on my journey so far. I knew I had to keep listening.

After careful thought, I decided to move into a home and set up a studio. One half of the home would be the Yoga studio; the other, I would live in. This place was perfect, quiet, and had a wonderful garden front and back. It was a short walk to the beach, and I was allowed to have an animal. This is when Bubbles, my cat, and I found each other. The conversation I had with my friend Thomas had manifested and I was now living the life that I had intended.

My intention was to stay in this home for one year and then move to a commercial Yoga studio. After one year, I found a wonderful space for that. I renovated it and built my beautiful space—what an adventure! So much hard work, so many long days and late nights, but my dream was finally here.

Throughout my life, I had always manifested whatever I intended in my heart. Whatever I felt really strongly about, whether it was positive or negative, I brought it into my life. This, I can very clearly see now.

My first year in the new studio was big! I had worked so hard, and I had little time for myself, so I decided to go on a retreat to Thailand for a few weeks. Bali was my last Yoga holiday, and that was when I had just finished my Yoga training. It was time to give back and nurture myself, to reconnect and ground myself. Ah, what bliss I enjoyed! I returned home rejuvenated and alive and ready to begin a new year.

What a fantastic start to 2013. I had spent the previous year building my new studio, moving in, and expanding my business, and I had also created a Yoga teacher training course of my own, launched in March 2013. Such a gift to be not only teaching Yoga, but now I was teaching beautiful students to become teachers of the art themselves!

Meditation was my saving grace. In the Gold Coast, I was part of a beautiful group that was part of an international community called Oneness. My meditation practice with Oneness had allowed me to heal so much of my past trauma. It allowed me to see what was within me that was really holding me back from living a wonderful, free, abundant life. In fact, meditation is what started me on my Yoga journey; a friend introduced me to transcendental meditation when I was just twenty years old.

Another place I had always longed to travel to was India. There, I got the opportunity to visit the Oneness University in Chennai, India, for a month of deepening and silence, after the workshops of my first Yoga training course were complete. This was a time of deep, profound spiritual awakening for me, and I returned home with so much genuine gratitude for what I had just experienced.

The next few months, I set many intentions that just kept manifesting. I spent my time in deep meditation whenever I was not teaching and took myself on such a wonderful journey to my core. I allowed myself to feel and experience anything that I needed, buried deep in my unconscious mind. I received so much insight and inner wisdom during this time, and I decided I had to return to India to embark on some training at the end of the year.

India the second time around was even more magical. The teachings given to me and the other participants were so sacred that I was reduced to tears of gratitude many times while there. I felt so honored and blessed to be a part of something so powerful, healing, and beautiful. I returned home with a deeper feeling of connection to all that is and a beautiful sense that everything is perfect. Everything is just as it's meant to be.

The months that followed gave me an opportunity to really apply all that I had learned from my trips to India. I allowed myself to sink into the sacred teachings and watch my thoughts, words, and actions. Inner integrity was my intention. I practiced aligning what was within me to what I was putting out into the world. I knew I wanted to, and I needed to walk my talk if I was to honor my higher self. This level of practice gave me so much insight as to how I was really playing this game called life. I saw how I wasn't showing up the way I genuinely wanted to. When I saw this, I was so grateful because I knew I had the power to change it. I had the power to change whatever I needed to so that I would be the most wonderful person I could possibly be.

Yoga has been my life raft when I was stuck out at sea in a world of pain and sorrow. It allowed me to see the light shining within me, and it also allowed me to accept the darkness within me and to know that I am both: light and dark. See, that is the wonderful thing about Eastern philosophy: it embraces paradox, for without darkness, we wouldn't cherish the light; without our pain, we wouldn't feel gratitude for the good.

My life has been filled with so many twists and turns, so many ups and downs. So much adventure, travel, and wonderful, inspirational people who guided and helped me on my journey. Through hard work, dedication, focus, and belief in that infinite force within me, I have been able to overcome so much. And you know what the funny thing is? I know this is only just the beginning. I know that the best is yet to come. I know each morning I wake up that I can enjoy each moment. I can feel every moment. I can live and experience life just as it is: the good and the bad. When we resist what is happening, that is when we suffer. If there is no resistance, there is no suffering.

About the Author

Melanie is a writer, Bhakti Yogini, avid reader, Oneness trainer, and Reiki Healer. Yoga is Melanie's passion, and she owns a beautiful Yoga studio on the Gold Coast called Golden Yoga. Melanie lives on the Gold Coast by the beach with her beautiful cat, Bubbles, and enjoys a peaceful, quiet life. Bringing the gift of Yoga to her students is a passion fulfilled for Melanie, which she cherishes every day.

http://www.goldenyoga.com.au

The Long Way Around

Morgan Barkus

"Some bloom where they're planted, while others transform in a process that takes them many places, and in the end they take off like a butterfly. Free."

There I was, standing at the top of the stairs with the cordless phone in my hand, just having hung up with a friend from high school. She had told me she was going to another party so wouldn't have time to attend mine. She was sure this other party wasn't something I would be interested in going to, as I didn't drink alcohol.

Twenty-one years old, I realized I hadn't spent much time learning how to socialize, so I was terribly isolated from my peers. I had spent much of my time maintaining a perfect 4.0 GPA and holding down several jobs during the summers. I was disciplined with money and down right rigid when it came to my health and weight. I counted every calorie, never ate foods I had deemed inappropriate for maintaining my thin frame, and obsessively made time to work out five days a week. I felt like my life was in perfect working order. Looking back now, I would say I was more like a machine, devoid of happiness. I was disconnected from my soul.

As I stood alone at the top of the stairs, my parents and a handful of their friends were in the kitchen. They were laughing and joking, drinking and eating. My brother was playing video games with a group of his friends. I was the only one without any guests, and it was *my* party. It was my graduation party for earning the first of various higher education degrees. In that moment, there at the top of the stairs, I was suddenly overwhelmed by my emotions. I had been so put together, and for what? What did I have to show for it? I was left feeling lost, hurt, lonely, sad, and reckless. These feelings were intense. They weren't good feelings, and how I handled them was even worse.

Pivotal moments are often assumed to be positive, but there are negative ones too. Often, there is a main event that changes someone's life forever. Not for me. Call me a slow learner, but I always seem to take the long way around. I have had several pivotal moments in my life that triggered transformation, and after struggling mentally, physically, and spiritually for over a decade, everything finally came together. Only now do I feel the safety and security of stability. After many years of wondering if I would ever recover from my depression and let go of my unhealthy coping mechanisms, I feel happier and more complete than I ever have in my life.

For years, after that day at the top of the stairs, I abused food to drown my depression. I turned to sex in an attempt to distract myself from my feelings of hopelessness. Partner after partner, I was trying to find the one that would make me feel like I mattered or had value. Physically connecting with strangers proved to be nothing but dangerous, both emotionally and in terms of my health. Food seemed the safest escape, seeing how I was never much for drugs or alcohol. The number of times I sat in front of a movie with a bag of golden Oreo cookies and my favorite pint of ice cream, eating until I fell asleep, would be difficult to even guess. When I was at my worst, I would eat the foods that brought me comfort until I felt sick, and then I would stand in the kitchen making myself throw it all up. That was my existence, and it was dark. I felt hopeless and empty.

I saw a therapist, and I had a few appointments at an eating disorders clinic. I worked with a nutritionist for a while. I found a twelve-step program for people struggling with emotional eating problems, I attended more therapy, and many times I contemplated suicide. I didn't want to commit suicide—I didn't really want to die. What I wanted was for the pain to go away. I wanted to stop fighting with myself. I wanted to wake up in the morning and be grateful to be me, not afraid of what I might do to myself that day. I wanted to feel *free*.

Three major components have been necessary for me to take this journey: mental health, physical health, and spiritual health.

Getting my mental health in check started when my mom gave me a copy of Louise Hay's book *You Can Heal Your Life*. I read that book multiple times, and when I took the time to write positive affirmations every morning, my negative self-talk started to disappear. Reading this book and incorporating positive affirmations into my daily routine has enabled me to not only change what I feed my subconscious mind, but to also shift my frame of mind if and when I need to. How I feel about and react to my life really is a choice.

I am a personal development junkie now, so I read many books on self-improvement, books on relationships, and books on advancing myself professionally. Four books that have served me well are *The Slight Edge* by Jeff Olson, *The Success Principles* by Jack Canfield, *The Secret* by Rhonda Byrne, and *The Power of Your Subconscious Mind* by Joseph Murphy. Each of these books has been instrumental in helping me achieve a state of mind that keeps me grounded, positive, and motivated.

The mindset exercises I do each day include reading aloud the positive affirmations I have written out on index cards, standing in the mirror in my Wonder Woman pose for at least two minutes, and repeating the five words I would like to embed into my subconscious, like a mantra each night, before I fall asleep.

I am in the mental health field but never was a fan of pharmaceuticals. I was of the belief that anyone could get over anything without the aid of synthetic drugs. What I came to realize, particularly after reading the book *Eat, Pray, Love*, is that even the most resilient people sometimes need the help of medication. It was a scary and nerve-racking decision on my part, but I made an appointment with a psychiatrist. A low dose of an anti-depressant was prescribed—and as reluctant as I was to follow through on actually taking the medication, I did. I am grateful and comforted by the effects. I am also proud of myself for taking action despite my fears about what people would think.

Attending to mental health takes courage and faith, and I hope that my honesty in revealing this part of my recovery encourages others to reach out for the help they need. Even if it isn't for a lifetime, sometimes our brain chemistry needs a little tweaking, and there is no shame in taking advantage of the resources available.

Physical health, for me, meant choosing a realistic workout plan, and then staying consistent with it. In the past, I was obsessive with fitness, whereas now I seek balance. I hired a health coach to teach me how to incorporate more vegetables into my diet, and I committed to working out three times per week, doing something I enjoyed rather than what I felt like I should do. I meditate when I feel like it, and I do Yoga when I have time. No longer do I put strict expectations on myself nor do I have an all-or-nothing mentality. I feed my body with clean food most of the time, and when I want a decedent piece of cheesecake or a big bowl of pasta, I indulge. Staying active and feeding my body with healthy foods keeps me feeling energetic and happy.

There are days I don't want to follow through on my commitment to my physical health, but I remind myself how amazing I feel when I do, and I power through. After coming as far as I have, making the healthier choices are always worth it at the end of the day.

My health coach asked me about spirituality during one of our sessions. She stopped me in my tracks. I was raised to be open-minded, loving, compassionate, forgiving, and loyal, but my faith? I had never really thought much about my spiritual health. Now I know that nurturing my spirituality means following my heart. My heart is wild, hopeful, and full of aspirations and dreams, yet fears rejection, disappointment, and heartache. I feel most alive when I am designing my own life. I have wandered around for years, bouncing from one thing to another, trying to figure out what exactly it is I want to do with my life.

Getting my spiritual health in check has meant selling almost everything I owned and moving across the country to a place where the sun shines most of the time and the air smells of saltwater. It has meant exploring multiple career avenues before settling into my true passion for helping others through coaching and consulting. My spiritual health is strengthened when I am in the present moment as much as I remember to be, and when I listen to my intuition. Feeling healthy spiritually has meant finding my purpose and staying true to it no matter how rough the road gets.

That feeling of freedom I wanted is finally my reality. The floodgates are open, and gratitude and joy run through me every day.

What I have learned after struggling with myself for over a decade is that this gratitude and joy is not a destination. It is a journey, a journey that I must believe in, nurture, and practice every day.

About the Author

Morgan Barkus is a personal development and relationship expert and a health consultant. She has a Master's Degree in marriage and family therapy and belongs to the American Association for Marriage and Family Therapy and the American Association of Sexuality Educators Counselors and Therapists. Morgan is a life changer, fashion worshiper, dance and fitness enthusiast, and hopeful romantic. She likes fast cars and loves to travel. Music of many genres is the soundtrack of her life.

http://www.morganbarkus.com

A Break in the Journey

Fiona McIlroy

A single diamond
Dazzles me.
A Banksia leaf
With a drop of dew
Brings my eye to you.

The arrow of hope
Pierces through
Fear to relief.

Morning sun
Can renew
An open heart.

Even one torn apart
Like that ancient tree,
By lightning
Can shine again.

How often one sets out on a journey to a destination, with the best advice and the most sensible intentions only to be stymied along the way by unexpected turbulence! My own story highlights the danger of following advice contrary to our own natural intuitions.

This was a journey broken by adversity. But, as it turned out, those very breaks, though painful, also gave time to "have a break"; reflect; and, thus, get back on track to what was my true journey to self-awareness, self-acceptance, and ultimately self-expression.

The story begins with a long horse ride from mountains to coast, which is a defining adventure in my life. The sky is a dramatic canvas on the Monaro plateau. From a car, a driver would notice signposts saying 38 km to Nimmitabel. From horseback, small flurries of cockatoos in a dead tree or a cirrus cloud resembling an angel become markers of interest.

Time passes by slowly, but the heartbeat is as regular as the sound of hoofbeats on the gravel. I learned to be fully present to every flutter, every call, every air current. Being anchored on the five-day journey with my horse was a healing experience. The man I loved had left me with no explanation—just emptiness. But now I felt connected to the world around me. His absence was no longer a cold blade to the heart. The presence of life in its many forms warmed me and the trusting bond between the horse and I felt deeply nourishing. Her ears twitched as I sang to the rhythm of her step. I was learning how to recover from pain and loss by taking a risk in trusting myself.

People who cared about me said that what I wanted to do was dangerous and that I needed to prepare for months to go on a long ride. But I needed to move interstate, and the simplest way was by horse. Besides, I had secretly dreamed of such an adventure. Now was the time to live the dream. This was the peak of my healing story. Now, to go back in time . . .

I had long been obsessed by horses—drawing them on every cover of my school books. Luckily, my parents responded by letting me have my own horse. I went on long rides through the bush in the backblocks with a friend. We jumped fallen logs, opened gates, and rescued koalas. This was my real life, even though riding was only possible on weekends since I had to travel three hours to and from school.

My parents had moved me to an elite private girl's school to get me away from danger. I was a survivor of sex abuse at the tender age of five, resulting in surgery. The first break in my journey left me with deep shame and fear. The long hours of train travel to and from school were a means of processing difficult feelings and regaining my sense of self. I was also impressionable to others' beliefs and wishes, so I needed time alone to know my heart and mind.

I was a poor fit for an elite Church school; I was shy and anxious—not an overt rebel, but not a conformist. The principal tried to hobble me, but I found harbor with music, art, drama, and poetry. It was clear even then that I would always be a seeker of life with all its peaks and troughs.

Being tied to my horse led to close encounters with life; death and loss came in the package too. My returning trust in the Universe was severely shaken when my first pony, Silver, died suddenly; the vet told me to bring a rug and bucket of feed. Minutes later, he rang to say Silver had died. I ran around the house, tearing curtains down and howling, until I had to be locked in my room.

The horse was also a vehicle of learning to trust my intuitive purpose on the life journey. My five-day journey from East Gippsland across Monaro to the South Coast empowered me in a larger sense. I had decided to move without a horse float because an outdoor adventure was key to restoring my sense of confidence. Together, we survived a drought with just tea, oats, and rice in a couple of saddlebags. Necessity plus intrinsic motivation are true confidence-builders!

A foal was born from the long ride after a one-hour tryst with a colt on a farm along the Kybean way near Nimmitabel. I believe the long journey made my horse fit, despite the vet saying she was too old to have another foal. Miracles happen when we are traveling our own path willingly. Perhaps the foal symbolizes the birth of my true self.

There were more bumps and breaks ahead in my journey to come, and times when the break (forced or otherwise) enabled me to reflect on how to take the "right" path while being gentle to myself.

Cutting short my academic study, I spent several years on the pioneering edge of the new settler movement in beautiful, remote places. I had healed myself on the five-day ride. My horse, Katy, was a steady true friend. We continued to travel great distances from remote community to community in the face of challenges of fire, flood, and isolation. But after a year, I realized I needed to find a job.

I heard my physicist father's voice repeating, *You need to get a meal ticket. Be a classroom teacher!*

Being close to the land far away from urban areas, writing poetry, riding a horse instead of driving a car, and saving forests could never amount to a meal ticket. His voice just spoke plain common sense.

This is the most bruising shattering experience of my life I wrote after my first day of high school teaching, when I attempted and failed to get a class of Year 8 to listen to poetry. The next night, at a teacher's party, a balcony railing collapsed, and I fell six feet, fracturing my spine. The impacted nerve from the injury gave me chronic pain. The doctor didn't recommend having a child. It seemed as though my life with the horse and living on the land were also shattered, but I went back to my heart place less independent, yet determined to live a life more attuned to my real needs.

It took two car accidents before I stopped trying to teach high school (I was a slow learner!).

A persistent desire to trust others meant a few falls off the cliff were likely. My family referred to me as the Pollyanna of the family. *Hopelessly naïve,* my brother might say, *but so starry-eyed you can't argue!*

This, I believe was my gift: always seeking new paths in uncharted territory, never shutting down my desire to experience life in an open-hearted way. If we are endowed with a gift, I feel we are tested and challenged to bring it into the light and make it shine.

Three children later, I moved to Canberra as a single parent and began to work as a facilitator and adult educator. Before I knew about "life coaching" as a profession in 1999, I designed my business card: "Inspire ACT—helping people act on their true goals." I finally realized I had teaching talent, but it did not include crowd control!

Now that I look back on the timing and severity of my accidents, the breaks in my body and spirit, they did not occur from extreme sport; indeed, riding my horse never broke my bones, as many friends assumed it would. The accident was always at a time of stress, when my goals were at cross-purposes with my natural bent. "Something's got to give" as the old adage goes. I am not a literal believer in the New Age "you create your life" maxim. This assumes too much power over our lives. I think there is an interplay between our choices and our environment. Trying to defy the force of gravity is a good metaphor for how I learned (through a crash course) to get in sync with my own nature.

The flip side of an intention to enable others to achieve their true goals is that one can override one's own needs. Those needs will reassert themselves in unexpected ways.

If we are on a journey to wellness, we need to take our own side. If we don't break the journey to reflect how we truly feel in our heart of hearts, the journey could break us.

Now, over time, I have gradually evolved the right balance between self-care and giving to others. I am as healthy as any grandparent in her late sixties, enjoying outdoor activity, family, and friends. Massage keeps the body pain-free, and poetry keeps the spirit alive. I love working with others to help them achieve that balance (without breaking any bones!).

About the Author

Fiona McIlroy is a published poet, a life coach, and a mediator, who loves to expand her horizons, and is fascinated by the natural world. She enjoys inspiring others to live a life aligned to their values and dreams. Fiona runs workshops called "Sea Change" and "Steer Your Career". Poem originally published by Ginninderra Press, 2009.

http://www.inspireact.com.au

The Gift of Breath

—⊗⊗⊗—

Kate Pamphilon

I t was a presence in my life before I knew its name. It visited me in the morning before I took a conscious breath. Trying to breathe. It was the transition from dream-state to reality that would trigger it. It felt unfair. I didn't have a chance if my day began clouded by it. *Hello, anxiety. I know you well!*

My path to wellness is a story of moving past a state of disconnect, insecurity, and fear to a place of connection, breath, and love. Today, I thrive on connected participation. Be it with others, energy, Spirit, and Earth, or self, I now know that feeding my spirit nourishing thoughts, emotions, and actions will ultimately feed Universal Spirit. Each soul is connected in the web of life. Imagine each act of love, compassion, and kindness that you do, including those directed to yourself, touching the lives of others in our world; likewise, their love is your love.

Have you ever felt scared, unsafe, or in real danger? Like walking down a dark alley alone. This is how many of us experience anxiety, as a sense of being incredibly vulnerable. Anxiety is the body and mind in a state of survival or fight/flight: heart racing, shallow quick breaths, tingling limbs, and a cloudy mind. *Run. Run. Run!* There is an invisible bubble of pressure around you, one of constriction, and you can't seem to step out if it. The bubble goes where you go. Your senses are muted. It's difficult to piece together information of any kind. You're in a state of contraction and the pressure is immense, and you feel naked and exposed. Your body shuts down to minimal functionality to enable you to simply run, run, run.

During childhood, my respite from anxiety was to throw myself into sport and theater. Although these activities can trigger anxiety for me, I found safety in the rhythm of basketball. I had a team; I wasn't alone. Theater was pure escapism. Naturally, I was terrible at improvisation! For scripted plays, however, I found comfort in exploring the life of another, the (mostly!) predictable nature of scene by scene. I had a cast and crew.

As I grew, so too did my anxiety. I was a sensitive soul and always wondered, "Was this to be my weakness?" By the time I reached the end of high school, my mother was sending me off to class with a small and discreet bottle of flower essences. Whenever I felt my anxiety surfacing, I would take a few drops until the symptoms eased. To this day, I still use flower essences as support.

My anxiety peaked as I went through university and adopted a "work hard, play hard" attitude. It was during this time that I realized I couldn't tackle my anxiety alone. I went to a counselor, naturopath, and Reiki Master where I was taught breathing techniques and began to understand anxiety.

There was a quiet calling, a whisper in my ear—persistent and assured. Waiting and listening with a sense of knowing.

After graduating, I jumped into the deep end of life. One of the greatest gifts my parents gave me was exposing me to the vast expanse beyond the town I grew up in. The challenge for me was to leap with faith despite my fears. I was short of breath and dizzy with wonder of what lay ahead. I knew if I wanted to live, to truly do what made my heart flourish, then I had to take on what my body feared most: to go it alone in the world.

As I traveled through Europe with a friend, the historical architecture, varying accents, and even tripping on a cobbled stone took my breath away. The dark, the light, the colored, and the gray— all beautiful to me. As we ventured on the train, we would sit in silence, breathing in each town, its people, its paths, and its stories. We had very little money, yet we happily absorbed our surroundings. I learned what it meant to exist in the present moment—to stop and connect with all my senses. When I was in this state, I found that I could sense much more than what I could see or touch. It was the magnificence of the connection to all things, to walk the earth with strangers, animals, and friends, and to know that we're all one. My anxiety began to show cracks. I was able to see that I was not broken or exposed. I could be open, strong, and centered. The stage or the court was not my foundation; Mother Earth and Spirit were. And they are everywhere. Was my sensitivity, perhaps, a gift?

Over the years, I slowly cracked away at the shell of anxiety that clothed my body. It wasn't an easy path and it wasn't a smooth one either, and at one stage I became bulimic as I tried to replace the returning sense of isolation and self-judgment with sugar. When I returned to Australia, I looked in the mirror and made a conscious choice to acknowledge my body as the temple of my soul. I took my shoes off and felt Mother Earth between my toes. I came back to her to heal. My challenge now was to live each day, safe in the knowledge that both Mother Earth and Universal Spirit were within me, as were the resources that I needed for survival.

There was a quiet calling, a whisper in my ear—persistent and assured. Waiting and listening with a sense of knowing.

In my thirties, I realized that my "successful" career path was numbing my mind, body, and spirit. I had tried many types of complementary medicine. The holistic approach to wellness resonated with my sense and understanding of the world. I just never thought that I could practice it myself. I was too focused on experiencing the beauty of the world, and my anxiety held me back from believing in my potential and truth.

However, within minutes of my first kinesiology balance, I had the feeling *this is it!* Kinesiology encompassed all that I knew to be at the core of healing and being. Not only did it work with every aspect (my physical body, physiology, emotions and thoughts, and Spirit), but it also worked from a point of energy. I was always playing with energy, even as a child—trying to feel someone without touching them. My sensitivity had felt like a curse, but I then began to understand it to be a gift.

As the practitioner talked to my body and subconscious, and as she balanced my energy system, I felt a sense of release, of freedom, and of connection. For the first time since I could remember, I was breathing with my whole self—calm and relaxed. And then *there was that quiet calling, a whisper in my ear, persistent and assured. Waiting and listening with a sense of knowing.* The Universe had everything in place for me to step truly into my soul work.

Today as a practitioner, kinesiology still takes my breath away, even after all these years. I am amazed at the synchronicity of a client's life and what their body talks of in a session. I am a facilitator to a person's own innate healing abilities. There's nothing more rewarding and empowering than to feel a client own their wellbeing.

The cloud of anxiety is exactly that: a cloud. It can pass. It does not own or define you. Find your triggers, and seek out what brings you peace and bliss. Beneath the noise and the pressure is the gentle voice of your spirit, your heart. But the cloud can return just like mine did. It hit me harder than ever before. The birth of my first child was lengthy and exhausting, and, although thankfully ended in the safe arrival of a beautiful spirit, I didn't fair so well. Through a lack of understanding of Post Natal Anxiety and Depression (PND) and an utter shame of what I was going through on the inside, I suffered in silence. When the despair became too much, I spoke up enough to ask my partner to move our family to be near my parents.

After only twelve months of new motherhood, I found my voice. It was another mother who had the strength to mention her own battle with PND that had me raising questions. One of the most common symptoms of PND is anxiety. I was scared to be alone at home with my baby; the silence and isolation had me screaming internally. One of the greatest gifts was joining a local support group that helped me understand and accept what had been happening.

I practiced the art of mindfulness. I learned to take a compassionate step backwards, which gave me the space I needed to calm down. Exercise became a way to release pent-up emotion and stress, to process my day, and to feel free.

To say, "I'm not OK", "I'm not coping", or "I don't think I can do this" is not shameful. You're simply saying, "I am human." Barely a week passes when I don't work with a child or adult to help heal their anxiety. My work in complementary medicine has become an extension of who I am. I have learned through my path from constriction to expansion that I am my own healer. Every day I experience and learn what it means to be present and connected to Spirit, and, in turn, I am grounded in my body and Mother Earth, powerful and intuitive. Seek your truth, your wisdom, and your love. Know that this is what connects us all. Know that you are not alone. Know that you are your own healer. And of course . . . breathe.

About the Author

Kate Pamphilon is a kinesiologist based in Canberra, Australia. Kate's soul work is to help others connect to their spirit and reach their full potential. Through working with a client on all levels, she is able to facilitate understanding, love, and acceptance of self. Kate facilitates workshops, offers online consultations and her blog "Holistic by Nature", and has an international following as she shares the wisdom and techniques of complementary medicine.

http://www.holisticnature.com.au

Get Published

Discover the World's #1 Book Publishing Service for Authors, Speakers, Entrepreneurs, and Thought Leaders

Interested in sharing your own story? There is more than one way to get published.

Through www.AlskaPublishing.com, we can help you share your inspiring journey through one of our upcoming compilation book series.

Alternatively, if you're ready to create your own book, we can help you get published at www.Verbii.com with zero contracts, zero exclusive agreements, and zero royalty splits.

Verbii.com is an independent self-publishing service that empowers authors with *complete* publishing control and an entire team of professional artists turning your book vision into a masterfully designed reality in just 60 days or less.

Experience the easy, game-changing book publishing solution you've been waiting for by going to www.Verbii.com today.

Also by Sarah Prout & Sean Patrick Simpson

All Älska Publishing titles can be found through the www. AlskaPublishing.com portal or requested from your local bookstore (and found through online bookstores as well).

Books

Adventures in Manifesting: Success and Spirituality
Adventures in Manifesting: Health and Happiness
Adventures in Manifesting: Passion and Purpose
Adventures in Manifesting: Healing from Within
Adventures in Manifesting: Love and Oneness
Adventures in Manifesting: Soulful Relationships
Adventures in Manifesting: Conscious Business

Kindle and iBooks

Each of the Adventures in Manifesting titles above can also be purchased via the Amazon Kindle or iTunes iBook formats.

About Sarah Prout
& Sean Patrick Simpson

Sean Patrick Simpson

Sean is the co-founder of both Älska Publishing and Verbii.com, who thrives on leading the Älska team and growing the company with his wife, Sarah. A musician and singer at heart, Sean has had his music played in over thirty countries after creating an album for the Fox Sports networks. If you look closely enough, you might even notice him singing a little ditty in the movie *Anchorman*.

Sarah Prout

Sarah Prout is the founder of SPROUT Magazine. Her love for metaphysics, design, and business empowerment shines through in her writing and teachings. Since 2006, Sarah has built an impressive international media and client portfolio inspiring people to create their own reality. Sarah reaches over 55,000 followers in over twenty-four countries around the globe with heartfelt, vibrant, and empowering advice about love, business, and style.

You can connect with Sarah and Sean at any of the sites you feel most inspired to discover.

http://www.AlskaPublishing.com (Home-site)

http://www.Verbii.com (Conscious Publishing for Conscious Authors)

http://www.SproutMag.com (SPROUT Magazine – Lifestyle Empowerment for Women)

http://www.SarahProut.com (Sarah's personal blog)